Revolutionaries at Sony

Revolutionaries at Sony

The Making of the Sony PlayStation and the Visionaries Who Conquered the World of Video Games

Reiji Asakura

McGraw-Hill

New York   San Francisco   Washington, D.C.   Auckland   Bogotá
Caracas   Lisbon   London   Madrid   Mexico City   Milan   Montreal
New Delhi   San Juan   Singapore   Sydney   Tokyo   Toronto

McGraw-Hill

A Division of The McGraw·Hill Companies

1 2 3 4 5 6 7 8 9 0 DOC/DOC 0 9 8 7 6 5 4 3 2 1 0 9

ISBN 0-07-135587-1

PlayStation® is a registered trademark of the Sony Corporation. All Rights Reserved.

English translation rights arranged with IDG Communications Japan through Japan UNI Agency, Inc.
English Language Translation Copyright by The McGraw-Hill Companies, Inc.
Project Management/Editing: David Kellar, President, Aetheria Co., Ltd;., Tokyo, Japan. Translation:Yuri Sakashita and Paul Rust, Bridge K.K., Yokohama, Japan.

Printed and bound by R. R. Donnelley & Sons Company..

This book was printed on recycled, acid-free paper containing a minimum of 50% recycled, de-inked fiber.

McGraw-Hill books are available at special quantity discounts to use as premiums and sales promotions, or for use in corporate training programs. For more information, please write to the Director of Special Sales, Professional Publishing, McGraw-Hill, Two Penn Plaza, New York, NY 10121-2298. Or contact your local bookstore.

CONTENTS

ACKNOWLEDGEMENTS

Ken Kutaragi and I first met a few years ago when I was a moderator and Mr. Kutaragi was a panelist at a technology symposium. I have interviewed many engineers and many business executives over the years, but I have never met one who has such clear vision, who speaks with such a rich vocabulary, and who possesses such great confidence based on personal accomplishments. I thought that this outspoken man must represent a new style of entrepreneur at Sony, where people are noted for being individualists.

From that day on, I dreamed of piecing together the PlayStation story with Mr. Kutaragi, and this book is the fulfillment of that dream. The story is a lesson for all of us: It is the story of what can be achieved with commitment, passion, and the will to overcome obstacles, of what can be achieved by a person with the wits to develop and implement an original business model.

Gathering the material to write this book was an extraordinarily exciting experience for me. I would like to thank everyone who gave their valuable time to be interviewed. Mr. Kutaragi graciously granted me many hours of interviews over several sessions. Teruhisa Tokunaka, Shigeo Maruyama, and Akira Sato of Sony Computer Entertainment were also most generous with their time, as were Norio Ohga and Tamotsu Iba of Sony. I also thank the executives of the various other companies in the game industry who helped me in this project.

A special thank-you goes out to author Mr. Akihiko Joshima, who provided me the opportunity to write this book; to Mr. Kozo Hiramatsu, president of IDG Communications Japan; and to Mr. Jun Awano and Mr. Masanori Seki, assistant editors-in-chief at IDG.

-September 18, 1998
Reiji Asakura

PROLOGUE

When Ken Kutaragi, vice president of Sony Computer Entertainment, is asked to identify the secret behind the creation and development of the PlayStation home game machine, he flatly declares: "I wanted to prove that even regular company employees—no, especially regular company employees—could build a venture of this scale with superb technology, superb concepts, and superb colleagues."

That the PlayStation business has been a tremendous financial boon for Sony Computer Entertainment cannot be denied. Consolidated annual sales of over $7 billion in only its fourth year. Total worldwide shipments, as of September 1998, of 40 million units. The PlayStation has taken on the vast Nintendo kingdom and become the world's leading game platform, both in perception and reality. There is no example of a comparable business that has shown such phenomenal growth for four years after start-up.

Says Sony chairman Norio Ohga: "Sony Computer Entertainment delivers such superb results with astonishingly few employees. Sony itself has much to learn from this example." In fact, Sony Computer Entertainment's contribution to Sony's consolidated profits has reached 23 percent. It is no exaggeration, then, to say that the PlayStation business undergirds Sony's profitability.

The PlayStation business has grown to its current size because it is a venture business conceived and carried out by salaried businessmen within a corporation. Kutaragi characterizes it this way: "Superb colleagues with superb technology and superb ideas accomplished it." The importance and potential of venture businesses have long been recognized, but in Japan the chance that an independent start-up or corporate spin-off venture businesses built on the Silicon Valley model will survive is low. Even if such a venture is successful, rapidly expanding it into a business operating on a global scale is extraordinarily difficult.

Kutaragi and his colleagues are truly deserving of the moniker "revolutionaries at Sony." Focusing on digital technology in the development of 3-D graphics for home-use game machines, Kutaragi's team set its sights on changing home entertainment in a fundamental way. They realized this objective with the PlayStation game platform. They went on to establish a revolutionary business model and utterly destroy the conventions by which the industry conducts itself.

The PlayStation can truly be termed a modern miracle. Exactly how did Kutaragi and his associates at Sony accomplish this remarkable feat?

KEY MEMBERS OF THE PLAYSTATION PROJECT

Ken Kutaragi

The father of the PlayStation and the hero of this book. An extraordinary engineer with a shrewd head for business. Currently Vice President, Sony Computer Entertainment Incorporated (SCEI).

Akira Sato

Demonstrated innovative ideas in the areas of distribution and marketing. Currently Vice President, SCEI.

Teiyu Gotoh

The outstanding designer responsible for the PlayStation console and controller. Currently Art Director, Sony Corporate Design Center.

Teruhisa Tokunaka

Responsible for overall management of the PlayStation project. Currently President, SCEI.

Shigeo Maruyama

A longtime and trusted confidant of Kutaragi who, along with Tokunaka, helped to move the PlayStation project forward. Currently Vice Chairman, SCEI, and President, Sony Music Entertainment.

Akira Tajiri

Supported the PlayStation project in the area of production technology. Currently Senior Managing Director, Technology Division, SCEI.

Masaaki Oka

A digital engineer who, along with Akio Oba, developed System G, the technological forerunner of the PlayStation. Currently Director, Architecture Research Division, Research and Development Division, SCEI.

Akio Oba

A digital engineer who, along with Masaaki Oka, developed System G, the technological forerunner of the PlayStation. Currently Vice Director, Architecture Research Division, Research and Development Division, SCEI.

Masashi Shimamoto

By pinpointing problems in the approach and activities of resellers, brought about thorough reform of the PlayStation distribution structure. Originally from Sony Music, currently Executive Director and Director, Sales Operations Division.

Masatsuka Saeki

Responsible for PlayStation promotions. Contributed to the rapid growth of the PlayStation through effective advertising campaigns. Currently Director, Advertising Division, SCEI.

Masaru Kato

As part of the international marketing effort, contributed to PlayStation's breakthrough in European markets. Currently Executive Director and Director, Administration Division, SCEI.

TOP MANAGEMENT OF SONY CORPORATION AT THE TIME

Norio Ohga

President, Sony Corporation, and commander in chief of the PlayStation project. Currently Chairman, Sony Corporation.

Tamotsu Iba

Executive Managing Director, Sony Corporation. Provided support and advice to the PlayStation project on capital and financial matters. Currently Vice President, Sony Corporation.

Nobuyuki Idei

Executive Director, Public Relations. Involved in Nintendo negotiations along with Kutaragi. Currently President, Sony Corporation.

1 CHAPTER

The Passion:
Ken Kutaragi—Always at
the Center of Controversy

THE ENCOUNTER WITH SYSTEM G

It was September of 1984, in a room at a Sony factory in Atsugi, Japan. An incredibly stunning picture was taking form on the monitor before Ken Kutaragi's eyes. On the screen was a computer-generated image of a person's face. The image changed shape at the touch of a slide control. The face would become bigger or smaller, merge with and then separate from adjacent objects.

The computer graphics system—called System G, the "G" from *gazo* (Japanese for "image")—was revolutionary in that it was capable of real-time 3-D texture mapping. The image not only moved instantly on command, but also appeared to be a substantive object. Even at that time such movement could be achieved after time-consuming calculations and command sequences, but this was the only system that could change the shape of an image instantaneously. Kutaragi, today a vice president of Sony Computer Entertainment, Inc. (SCEI), was astonished that the image moved at the touch of a switch. He recalls, "It was far more advanced than state-of-the-art graphics systems of the time. It was awesome. I was really impressed that such a thing existed."

System G was a geometric engine for 3-D processing, developed for broadcasting networks. An example of a current application is its use by Nippon Television Network Co. to change the size of computer-generated faces in the popular TV program *Denpa Shonen*.

At the time, the Information Processing Research Center (now disbanded) was the nerve center of Sony's research in digital signal processing. The center's work spanned a broad range of digital technologies, including data compression, networking, and communication protocols. Kutaragi was one of its researchers. It can only be described as fate that Kutaragi was working there, that the System G prototype had just been completed, and that the paths of this man and this technology had crossed.

As Kutaragi watched the freely moving image produced by System G, inspiration struck. "What a powerful game machine we could make with System G," he thought. This was the moment when the concept of a system that later blossomed into the PlayStation was born: a graphics computer that anyone can use. What fascinating, exciting games people could play if System G were combined with a game machine. The Famicom (short for family computers) game machines popular at the time displayed simple, two-dimensional images, but their entertainment value was outstanding. How wonderful it would be, thought Kutaragi, if the Famicom standard could be enhanced with System G.

Kutaragi had always been fascinated by computer graphics. The subject of his university thesis was how to apply computer graphics to medical equipment. The study explored methods of detecting abnormalities from CT-scanned X-ray images and individual hemoglobin shapes, and methods of extracting deformed cell nuclei and making them more visible. Because of his interest in computer graphics, he realized at once how revolutionary System G was.

But Kutagari's fascination went beyond computer graphics—he loved everything about computers. He bought all the game machines and PCs that he could lay his hands on. One of his chief interests was computer hardware, especially the application of semiconductor technology and microprocessors. "When I was a postgraduate researcher at university, Intel launched the 4004 and 8080 microprocessors," recalls Kutaragi. "As soon as they came out, I ...bought the world's first electronic calculator. It cost ¥100,000 ($1000) back then! It's a treasured antique now.

After I joined Sony, I bought a large-scale integrated circuit (LSI) circuit sample of the Ping-Pong game, assembled it, took it to a ski resort, and played with it in my room by plugging it into a TV. It was good fun."

Even so, his experience with computer games had not prepared him for System G; he had never before seen computer-generated images that moved so freely before his eyes, responding immediately to his commands. He thought it would be great if the technology was used to create a game machine.

Kutaragi had purchased a Famicom for his two-year-old son when it was released in 1983. He had played with it himself and found it great fun. "I tested it from a business perspective. I placed a Sony MSX and a Famicom before my son and observed him, waiting to see which he would choose. He chose the Famicom. He seemed to enjoy playing with it much more than the MSX. I was truly impressed by the Famicom."

The expression "from a business perspective" is typical of Kutaragi. He was exploring the business marketablility of the systems, and his child's preferences told him that it would be the Famicom, not the MSX, that would become popular with users.

What did he find impressive about the Famicom? Kutaragi explains, "In those days, the IBM PC displayed just one color: green. It was enjoyable enough playing the Ping-Pong game on that screen, but the Famicom went a step further and was truly revolutionary. PCs and Sony's MSX created eight-dot images, but the Famicom could produce single-dot images. I thought it was incredible. The software, Donkey Kong and Road Runner, was fun too, but my interest was more in the hardware."

That is why when Kutaragi encountered System G, he thought immediately of how much fun it would be to combine it with the Famicom, and why he resolved to do so.

FIRST JOB WITH SONY: LEADER OF A REBEL GROUP

Kutaragi did not hit upon the idea of combining System G and the Famicon purely from an engineer's point of view. Whenever he came across an interesting idea, his thoughts quickly turned to how the technology could be successfully commercialized.

This trait can be traced back to his upbringing. Kutaragi was born in Tokyo in 1950. His unusual surname comes from a town in Kumamoto Prefecture. His father, Takeji Kutaragi, was born in Kumamoto and moved with his family to Taiwan, graduated from Taipei University, and, with the help of relatives, opened Shinkodo, which would become the biggest bookstore in Taipei. He returned to Japan after the end of World War II and settled in Koto-ku, Tokyo, where he started a small printing shop. It was a business started in desperate conditions; he literally did not know where his next meal would come from.

As a young schoolboy, Kutaragi was expected to work in his family's printing business. As soon as he returned from school, Kutaragi made the rounds of customers, helped in the workshop, or made deliveries until 11 P.M. Although still a child, he worked hard day after day, too exhausted to do anything after work but fall into bed. Kutaragi recalls his childhood in this way: "Taking a long vacation and traveling with the whole family was a distant dream. My father always used to say that tradesmen have no holidays, but since there is no mandatory retirement, they can work all their lives."

Kutaragi was an A student at elementary school in every subject but two: physical education (he was not a robust child) and social studies. At times, his difficulties in these areas would bring out a certain kind of arrogance in the young Kutaragi. "My homeroom teacher told me I wasn't cooperative. I used to get mad, thinking I was being singled out." In some respects, however, the teacher's criticism was correct. Many years later, when Kutagari was starting up the PlayStation business, this personality trait would become a powerful driving force. It would not be inaccurate to describe it as the confidence of a talented loner, the strong will to complete a task in which he believed, regardless of the obstacles put in his way.

"My father did not trust the Japanese government at all. He didn't put his savings into a bank or post office account, but kept it all in cash. He had no confidence in Japan's social systems," says Kutaragi. When Kutaragi became a postgraduate researcher at university, his father became ill. The young Kutaragi took it for granted that he would carry on the family business, but his father said to him: "This business stops with me. You should look further ahead and do what you really want to do. We left Taiwan, so we have no relatives or influential contacts to help you, but I've managed to save some money. You can become a doctor or a lawyer—anything you want." By that time Takeji Kutaragi had indeed acquired enough assets to enable his son to pursue whatever career he wanted. He would say: "You're an adult now, so from now on you must choose your own future. Don't feel obligated to stay in the family business."

Kutaragi was proud to be the son of a tradesman. For him, working hard to make money was a given. He did not want to be a salaried worker or a civil servant. Nor did the idea of being employed by other people appeal to him. Because of his background, linking ideas to business came naturally to Kutaragi. It was a way of thinking to which he was born and bred.

Upon graduation, Kutaragi had a strong desire to start his own business, but he realized that a man just out of college was unlikely to enjoy quick success as an entrepreneur. Although such ventures are not uncommon today among recent graduates, they were unheard of in the mid-1970s. "I need business experience first. It won't be too late if I wait awhile before starting my own business," Kutaragi thought. "But more important, what do I really like to do? What do I excel at? It has to be electronics and computers. If that were my work, every day would be a delight. First I'll improve the skills I enjoy working with and acquire as much knowledge as possible."

Kutaragi had been interested in one company for a while: Sony. Today Sony is one of the most sought-after employers among Japanese college graduates, but at the time students had little interest in the company. Unlike most traditional Japanese companies, postwar Sony was a growth company that excelled in technology. Kutaragi had noticed the company's magnificent-looking headquarters in Gotanda and its Central Research Institute in Hodogaya, Yokohama, and had read some stories about transistors written by Sony cofounder Masaru Ibuka. Kutaragi felt that at Sony he would be able to pursue his intellectual interests, and above all he approved of the apparent absence at Sony of education-based hierarchies and nepotism. He was also convinced that the company would have many talented employees to help him gain experience as an engineer.

Kutaragi told his academic adviser that he wanted to join Sony. The professor immediately agreed that it was a good idea: "Yes, Sony would really suit you. You would struggle in any other company, but you'd do well at Sony."

Kutaragi's fellow students were mainly eager to become civil servants, or join Japan's public telephone company (NTT Corp. before privatization) or one of the manufacturers of heavy electric equipment. It was considered eccentric to want to work for a consumer electronics firm. Kutaragi, born after the Second World War, certainly was eccentric—his willfulness showed in the fact that he was interested only in Sony.

He applied for a position with the company and quickly received notice of provisional acceptance. Kutaragi had never seen his father so pleased. Takeji Kutaragi was surprised and delighted that his son had found himself a job with Sony without benefit of family or personal connections. At the time Sony was ranked about fiftieth in popularity among students, far behind blue-chip firms such as Mitsubishi Corp. and Mitsui & Co., ranked first and second, respectively. "My father was pleased, though, because Sony wasn't a *zaibatsu*, nor part of the establishment. In other words, it wasn't a traditional Japanese company."

Ken Kutaragi joined Sony in 1975. Japan was in the midst of a recession following an oil shock, and the company had adopted a policy of hiring no new employees. However, realizing that a complete freeze in hiring would lead to problems in later years, the company decided to recruit a small number of employees, far fewer than it had in other years. Kutaragi was one of the chosen few.

The Sony employees who joined the company at the same time as Kutaragi were all quirky individuals. Kutaragi soon found himself their leader, because of his role in bringing them together. "I was the rebel leader," he confesses. "From the company's point of view, I was at the top of their blacklist."

When he started working for Sony, Kutaragi was horrified to find that few people did any actual work. It was the height of the spring labor offensive—an annual nationwide event that was popular in the 70s when there was widespread work stoppages. Assemblies were held, voices roared over loudspeakers in Gotenyama (Shinagawa Ward, Tokyo), and red flags fluttered in the wind. Kutaragi's personal experience had taught him that people should work, and his world was turned upside down by a culture that defined work as bad. Though dumbfounded by what was transpiring, he decided to ignore what was going on around him and enjoy the freedom his situation afforded him to pursue his vocation as an engineer. The first step, he decided, was to start working.

Kutaragi had vowed when he joined Sony to drive himself for ten years, and he worked hard to gain experience. He was blissfully unaware that his first decade with Sony would lead him toward the PlayStation concept. And destiny was about to lead him surely, unerringly, toward the Sony Information Processing Research Center in Atsugi.

CHARMED BY THE MAGIC OF DIGITAL SIGNAL PROCESSING

Kutaragi's first assignment at Sony was the First Development Division, which was developing display devices, including one called Trinitron. His first project saw him working on applied liquid crystal display (LCD) devices. In those days, companies had only just started developing LCD devices, and the only application for LCDs was in electronic calculator displays. Kutaragi immediately took up the challenge of developing a flat display and tried applying it to televisions.

In 1976, the year after he joined Sony, Kutaragi succeeded in displaying TV images on a 100×80–pixel matrix display panel. He also produced an LCD projector prototype, which involved shining light through an LCD panel and projecting the LCD image onto a large screen. Years later, this method would be adopted by various other companies, bringing great commercial success to their products.

In the end, Kutaragi's project did not see the light of day because of a power struggle at the time within the First Development Division between those promoting electroluminescence (EL) and those backing plasma as the next-generation display technology. New to the company, Kutaragi was unable to gain leverage with the existing power groups. More important, Sony had just developed a TV using its proprietary Trinitron technology, and there was no opportunity for an LCD TV to establish itself. Kutaragi recalls: "I didn't have a hope. It was very disappointing."

Undaunted by this setback, Kutaragi moved on to a new idea involving audio products, one of his hobbies. How about applying LCD to audio? He thought of making an LCD cassette deck peak-level meter. At the time there were volume unit meters (VU). VU meters with needles and optical peak-level meters, but high-performance meters were very expensive because of their intricate mechanisms. Kutaragi wanted to replace them with LCD meters. Instead of numerical displays, he wanted to use blue-and-orange bar graphs to display the different levels. He also used signal processing to enable the peak value to remain for a moment at the tip of the bar graph. Not only was this useful, but it looked distinctive and fun.

Kutaragi relates: "I was absorbed in assembling it and didn't notice Mr. Ibuka standing behind me observing my work. His eyes shone as he said, 'This is really good. Have you shown it to the guys in the Audio Division? If not, I'll contact them right away.' The following day, a group of people came down from the Audio Division and the idea was commercialized very quickly."

Although the LCD peak-level display was appealing to the eye, its high cost made it unsuitable for volume production. Cassette decks incorporating LCD displays were developed, but they were expensive. So Kutaragi changed his thinking, separating the ends from the means. His goal was to change all mechanical cassette-deck meters to digital bar graph meters. This meant there would be no need to use LCD; light-emitting diodes (LED), which performed the same function, would do just as well. Because the same signal processing was used, the peak-value display function could be retained.

The LED bar graph display was a great success, and the technology was immediately used in video-player sound meters as well. Other companies followed suit. Subsequently, many other uses were found for the device and Sony shipped 10 million units in total.

Kutaragi's early experience at Sony stimulated his interest in inventing. Having decided that all experiences were valuable in developing his career, Kutaragi began to indulge his fascination with making things. He was enthralled by the process of creating a new technology, giving it shape, and applying it to a product. Each step required creativity. The more ideas he incorporated, the more performance improved and his objectives were achieved. Even better was the knowledge that the creations he labored over could be enjoyed by many people. Kutaragi was hooked on the allure of providing the world with consumer products.

THE PASSION OF "WANTING TO CHANGE THE WORLD WITH MY OWN TECHNOLOGY!"

The development of a two-inch floppy disk by Sony led Kutaragi into a serious exploration of digital technology. For a time, an analog-storage two-inch floppy was used in the Sony Mavica, a magnetic-storage still-video camera promoted under the catchphrase "You don't need film anymore." Kutaragi explains: "The Mavica in those days used analog storage, so its signal-processing capability was limited. As for the two-inch floppy disk itself, even if it were to be permanently incorporated into the Mavica, demand would be extremely limited. But I thought there would be significant demand if it could be developed as a general-purpose floppy disk that directly stored digital signals."

So Kutaragi started working on error-correcting algorithms—programs that eliminate noise by correcting replay signal errors. At the time, optical disks such as CDs were prone to many reading errors that had to be corrected, whereas correction was considered unnecessary for magnetic media because the direct contact of the tape head provided an accurate reading. Kutaragi predicted that even magnetic media would become faster because of higher density and hence greater speed.

The Mavica's two-inch floppy's speed was 3,600 rpm. The endeavor to record at such a high speed naturally entailed a high risk of error, necessitating error correction. The development of error-correction devices was a fascinating area to Kutaragi, but he began to realize that he could not survive in the company by doing pure research in this field.

At the time, another Sony department was desperately trying to make the 3.5-inch floppy disk a de facto industry standard, in a furious race against rival Hitachi, Ltd., and its three-inch format. Two floppy-disk formats had been developed simultaneously within Sony; one was being pushed to become the industry standard, whereas the other had been developed by young engineers like Kutaragi in a project born of adventurism. Normally, the two formats would not be allowed to exist side by side, and the company would have to concentrate its efforts on one.

Kutaragi, however, had a vision. On May 31, 1985, the day when the company was scheduled to decide whether to continue with development of the two-inch floppy, Kutaragi's team and the team that developed the more mainstream 3.5-inch format confronted each other at a meeting. Those working on the 3.5-inch floppy disk were not happy about the work within Sony on the two-inch format. In the weeks leading up to the meeting, rumors had been rife that the two-inch project might be scrapped. To prepare for the meeting, Kutaragi's team had devoted their weekends and holidays to completing a prototype. During the meeting, as they eagerly demonstrated the prototype, they enthusiastically requested permission to proceed with development.. No decision to ax the project was made that day.

It was Kutaragi's tenth year at Sony. By then he had learned how to maneuver behind the scenes instead of confronting his rivals head-on. He believed that if the 3.5-inch floppy disk was destined to be a de facto standard, there was no reason the two-inch floppy disk could not be steered along the same path. His next strategy, therefore, was to propose to the Electronic Camera Council that the two-inch floppy be adopted as a digital data standard; he hoped to elevate it to the status of a standard industry format. He chaired a study group at the council and held working meetings twice a month.

Kutaragi's thinking was as follows: "Surely Sony can't ignore this format if it becomes a joint development theme for the industry, including top manufacturers such as Hitachi, Matsushita Electric, Fuji Photo Film, and Canon, rather than something developed by a small group within the company."

Around this time, Kutaragi's career as a Sony engineer suddenly became very eventful. He acquired the tenacity of an engineer in pursuit of a goal in which he believes, and the commitment to use every possible means to overcome complications and to complete a project once undertaken. Kutaragi had mastered a distinctive set of survival skills that in later years would see him through many detours and drive him to achieve victory against all odds in his quest to develop a game machine.

THE "DIGITAL HATERS" WITHIN SONY

The two-inch floppy disk was eventually adopted as an industry standard in the electronic product industry and subsequently incorporated into the Produce, Sony's Japanese word processor, and Sanyo word processors. Kutaragi's vision of developing high-speed floppy disk technology that applied error correction and high-density storage modulation technology had come to pass, and he had realized his goal of bringing to the world products he had created.

By then, however, Kutaragi was obsessed by a dream on a grander scale: digital signal processing. He had become aware of the potential of digital technology during his work on error correction. Kutaragi tried to persuade everyone he met that Sony had to embrace the challenge of digital technology. "The age of the computer is certain to come. To prepare for it, Sony must establish its own powerful digital technology and aim to move into the computer market."

At the time, few consumer products incorporated digital technology. Although today digital technology is ubiquitous, the only digital equipment available in those days was Sony's CD player, with analog long-playing recordings still mainstream in 1985. This relationship between CDs and LPs would be reversed a mere two years later.

As for PCs, Microsoft's MS-DOS had only just made its appearance and very few people purchased the difficult-to-use machines. Only the most dedicated geeks and specialist researchers emulated Kutaragi, who would build his own computer system by trial and error as soon as a microprocessor went on sale.

Before the two-inch floppy disk project, Kutaragi had had the opportunity to work with engineers of Sony's Audio Division when he was developing LCD level meters. At the time, semiconductor makers had come out with 4-bit control microcomputers and were selling them aggressively to equipment manufacturers like Sony. The problem was that even engineers confident in their ability to design analog circuits and small mechanical devices had no experience developing programs using small computers. Indeed, there was no equipment anywhere in the Audio Division for developing such programs.

Kutaragi set about developing a computer that would allow development of applications for different manufacturers' microcomputers using a single system. This was more than twenty years ago, before the launch of the IBM PC and Microsoft's operating system. The only operating system available was CP/M, a disk operating system for 8-bit CPUs. Kutaragi struggled through English-language manuals, ordered integrated circuits to design a board, loaded CP/M, and somehow managed to construct a computer.

From that point on, Kutaragi demonstrated his skill as an engineer. In a short time, he had written more than twenty different cross-assemblers for various manufacturers' 4-bit microcomputers. By now, he was becoming increasingly involved in software development as well as hardware. Following his lead, the engineers of Sony's Audio Division began developing applications using microcomputers, and soon had produced cassette-deck mechanical control and display programs.

Kutaragi taught groups of new employees in the Audio Division how to develop programs. Responding to engineers' requests, he and a colleague assumed joint responsibility for developing assemblers for new microcomputers, adding new assembler functions, and speeding up development programs. As a result, they were able to create an assembler development environment before the semiconductor manufacturers themselves, and to complete development more quickly. This gave Sony's audio-equipment design a significant advantage in efficiency, giving the company an ever-increasing edge over its rivals. This was to be of major importance in Sony's subsequent development of the PlayStation.

Kutaragi worked tirelessly on digital circuit design and the development of computer hardware and software at Sony. In part because only a few other Sony engineers had much expertise in this field, Kutaragi became convinced that he had to inject "digital culture" into Sony's corporate culture. He longed for Sony employees and management to understand the power of digital technology, which allows greater freedom to manipulate signals than is possible with analog technology, making possible a variety of technological advances.

Unfortunately, the Sony of that period was not receptive to this idea. On the contrary, the thinking among company brass was decidedly antidigital. Although the success of Sony's CD players gives the impression that its strength has long been digital technology, only recently has the digital revolution truly infiltrated the thinking of Sony engineers. In reality, Sony is still a strongly analog-oriented company. Although company president Nobuyuki Idei is now calling on the whole company to change direction under the slogan "Digital Dream Kids," this indicates only the effort needed to change Sony's deeply ingrained analog tradition.

Things were much worse in 1985. Whenever Kutaragi said he wanted to further the company's research in digital technology, every response was negative: "That's out of the question." "That's taboo at Sony." Even today, Kutaragi has not forgotten the words of a senior colleague at the First Development Division, his first posting at Sony: "I hear you want to develop digital technology, but you must never say that at Sony. You'll be transferred immediately." This remark clearly illustrates how digital technology was perceived at Sony in those days.

DATA PROCESSING RESEARCH LABORATORY ON THE FRONT LINES OF DIGITAL RESEARCH

The development and marketing of SOBAX, the world's first electronic calculator, which became the focal point of a price war and had to be withdrawn from the market, had left a scar on the sensitivities of Sony engineers. The traditional hierarchy of Sony engineers consisted of analog circuit engineers at the top, followed by mechanical engineers, and then structural engineers, who work on chassis and box design. Digital engineers were the lowest of all, several ranks below the structural engineers.

Moreover, the work of digital engineers at the time involved not digital signal processing or computer language development, but the design of control devices for video and audio equipment. These workers were known internally as "syscon engineers," and to call their role an underappreciated, behind-the-scenes support function is to understate the point. Although in theory their task was one of the most important parts of systems design, in practice they were but mere troubleshooters, somehow devising ways to make circuit designers' and mechanical engineers' last-minute designs function. Kutaragi's senior colleague's advice had been prompted by a desire to prevent a subordinate about whom he cared from falling in with such a lowly group.

In fact, this scenario was about to come true. One day, after the two-inch-floppy project had nearly wound down, Kutaragi was asked if he wanted to move to a division working on VCR system control. This was in the midst of the Betamax-VHS war, and at Sony making VCRs easier to operate was seen as the solution to improving their appeal to potential buyers. Kutaragi's ability as an engineer was well known in the company, and he was also a digital technology expert, which made him a very desirable commodity from the VCR Division's point of view.

"I was told that I had too much to say for myself, and I would learn to keep quiet if I worked in syscon," Kutaragi recalls. But he did not want to work with VCR system control and longed to work in digital signal processing research instead. His priority now was to further develop his skills as an engineer. So he consulted Toshio Doi, then a Sony director, a rising star in the management who was involved in the development of the NEWS workstation, highly powerful microcomputers used to perform very complicated calculations, usually for scientific, engineering, and design applications. Said

Kutaragi: "I want to do research in digital signal processing, and my long-terminterest is home computers." Doi advised him, "Go to Mr. Morizono."

"Mr. Morizono" was Masahiko Morizono, a vice president of Sony, whose broadcasting equipment team had achieved brilliant results at the plant in Atsugi. As the leader of the renowned "Morizono Corps," he was highly respected in the industry. Morizono listened patiently and sympathetically to Kutaragi's words, then sent him to Hirobumi Yoshida, director of the Sony Information Processing Research Center in Atsugi. Kutaragi was astonished that a digital technology research facility existed at Sony of which he had been unaware in all his time with the company.

The Atsugi facility was the main base for Sony's research-and-development effort in digital signal processing technology. It engaged in R and D of digital filters, digital signal processors (DSPs), and computer graphics. For Kutaragi, unappreciated at the VCR Division, the place seemed like Utopia. Convinced this was the place for him, he immediately applied for a transfer.

As though to head him off, however, the VCR Division issued Kutaragi an unofficial notice of transfer. If the transfer went ahead, he would have to do work he disliked and forgo learning more about digital technology. How frustrating for him—and just when he had finally discovered his calling at the Information Processing Research Center. But just then a telephone call from Masahiko Morizono again put him on the path toward his destiny. "I want to transfer you to the Information Processing Research Center," said the Sony vice president. To Kutaragi, it seemed like a last-minute reprieve.

Kutaragi was in his element at the center, and he absorbed a wide range of knowledge. He was passionate about his research work. Best of all, the center employed more than a hundred young and talented digital engineers. The place had an academic atmosphere that Kutaragi found stimulating and enjoyable.

Kutaragi explains: "At Sony, a new business that turned over 10 billion yen was considered a big success, but I wanted to start up a business that would become a new major income source for the company in the future. The approach I adopted was to create a business on a larger scale than what I could achieve on my own, or as a venture with a few other people; something possible only with a big company like Sony." This is a reflection of Kutaragi's exceptional talent. An ordinary engineer who moved to a research institute would aim to excel as a researcher and produce an invention, publish in academic circles and win acclaim, or earn an advanced academic degree. But Kutaragi's focus was business: starting up a new business on a grand scale.

Kutaragi's strength lay in the rare combination of research skill and business acumen that he possessed. The PlayStation project he launched some years later, which combined both 3-D computer graphics technology and a highly innovative business plan, reflected Kutaragi's dual personality as a businessman and a researcher in digital technology.

At a time when he was looking for the seeds needed to start an innovative business within Sony, Kutaragi happened to come into contact with System G computer graphics technology. He immediately thought that this, combined with the delights of the Famicom that so fascinated his son, would open up incredible new vistas in the world of games based on digital technology.

His goal line was set ten years ahead. Kutaragi always thought in terms of decades. He defined his first ten years with Sony as the time to polish his technical skills. In 1985, ten years after he joined the company, he encountered various innovative technologies and acquired many talented digital engineers as colleagues. In the next ten years he planned to let the technology take shape. He predicted, on the basis of a detailed technological forecast, that even a leading-edge technology like System G would be transformed into a consumer product in a decade's time.

Kutaragi had great faith in his prediction. He believed that in the mid-1990s, highly advanced technology like System G could be incorporated into products commonly used by consumers, and that children would be enthralled by the latest 3-D computer graphics games.

2 CHAPTER

"DO IT!": The Decision-Making Process

SHOCK ON THE TOKYO STATION PLATFORM

Kutaragi felt as if he had been struck on the head with a blunt instrument. It happened as he was about to board a Shinkansen (bullet train) on Platform 21 of Tokyo Station at 8:00 A.M. on May 29, 1991. His destination was Nintendo headquarters in Kyoto. There he would discuss details of the June 1 release of the CD-ROM–compatible Sony Super Family Computer ("Super Famicom") at the Consumer Electronics Show (CES) in Chicago. Nobuyuki Idei, Sony's director of public relations at the time, was waiting for Kutaragi on the platform and, memo in hand, gave him the startling news.

"Hey, Kutaragi, read this! Apparently Nintendo has torn up its contract with Sony and joined forces with Philips instead."

"What? You can't be serious!"

The two men immediately changed their Shinkansen reservation to a private compartment. On the train, they telephoned numerous contacts as they made their way to Kyoto. They even placed an international call to Philips, but were unable to obtain any corroboration of the news.

At the time, the relationship among Philips, Nintendo, and Sony was rather complicated. Philips was promoting the CD/I format, and Sony also had a CD/I team. The CD/I camp believed that the CD-ROM machine being developed by Kutaragi's team would hinder public acceptance of the CD/I format, since CD/I had been conceived as a home-use format and would be in direct competition in the game market with the CD-ROM machines made by Nintendo and Sony. Those involved in CD/I felt threatened and resolved to crush the Nintendo-Sony joint project at all costs.

Meanwhile, Nintendo was concerned that its business would eventually be taken over by Sony if Sony continued to drive product development. Although Nintendo was dominant

in the game-machine market, the company was fully aware that
Sony had a far superior research-and-development operation
and thus had the potential to outstrip its competitors in the area
of technological advancement.

Thus, Nintendo and Philips had a common interest. The
enemy of an enemy is a friend. These circumstances caused the
two companies to rapidly strengthen their relationship.
Unaware of all this, Kutaragi diligently fed information to the
Sony CD/I team, never imagining that a year later, Sony would
sever all ties with Nintendo.

Before they knew it, the train had arrived at the platform of
Kyoto Station. They proceeded by taxi to Nintendo's head office
near Tofukuji Temple. Both men sat glumly in the taxi without
uttering a word. At the Nintendo office, they met Minoru Arakawa,
president of Nintendo America. "What on earth is going on?" they
demanded. After a long silence, Arakawa said, "To be honest…it's
true." Then he fell silent again. Idei and Kutaragi demanded
details, but Arakawa would say no more. A tense atmosphere set
in. On being asked, "So what has happened to your contract with
Sony?" Arakawa finally spoke. He simply replied, "We will honor
the agreement." Arakawa's attitude was distant and unfriendly.
Since they were getting nowhere, Idei and Kutaragi gave up and
left the room.

On the journey back to Tokyo, Kutaragi recalled that their
last visit to Philips had been rather odd. Information leaked to
the press about the Super Famicom had resulted in a spate of
news articles and was causing a lot of speculation. At the
unveiling of the product at the Chicago CES, Sony intended to
announce that it planned to develop software for the game
machine mainly in the United States. Kutaragi and Sony's CD
personnel had flown to Holland on May 14 to explain the situation to Philips; Sony was obliged to discuss all CD formats
with Philips due to a contractual obligation.

The meeting at the Philips headquarters in Eindhoven had been strange and uncomfortable for everyone there. Kutaragi spoke at length about the products he had worked so hard to develop, but the Philips delegates barely reacted to the presentation and remained eerily silent.

Kutaragi later learned that at around the same time Nintendo was holding preliminary talks with Philips' CD/I (CD Interactive) staff, plotting to crush the Nintendo-Sony joint project. Even more shocking was the fact that although Sony's CD/I staff had detected Nintendo's intentions, they had not said a word to Kutaragi and his team. There was a clear struggle for supremacy between competing digital media within Sony.

When Kutaragi was informed of these machinations, he was incensed. At times such raw emotion can motivate a person to take decisive action. And there is no doubt that Kutaragi's fury, directed at the CD/I personnel of Nintendo and Philips who acted like gentlemen but plotted against Sony behind his back, became a driving force in his business dealings.

Why had Sony decided on a joint venture with Nintendo in the first place? Behind even that decision can be found some of the secrets to the success that characterized the development of the PlayStation.

WORKING TO SELL THE CONCEPT TO NINTENDO

"Why did they adopt something like this?" Kutaragi was astounded that Nintendo, which had developed the Famicom, had released a product that was so technologically retrogressive. His disappointment concerned the Disk System, unveiled by Nintendo on February 21, 1986. It was a Famicom data-storage peripheral; it took eight seconds to read the disk and three times longer, twenty-four seconds, to write to the disk.

"Technologically it was way behind. It was a 300 rpm disk with a capacity of just 64 kilobytes, and no random access. I just couldn't understand why they released it. The two-inch floppy that we developed had a speed of 3,600 rpm and a capacity of 1 megabyte. Nintendo's mask ROM cartridge expressed capacity in bits, so using their terminology, the floppy had 8 megabits of capacity, more than enough to contain the software in use at the time. We thought they used the Disk System because they didn't know this technology was available."

Kutaragi's interest in Nintendo stemmed from his admiration of the Famicom. It was typical of him that when a product or idea caught his attention, he would immediately pay a visit to the people responsible for it. In the past, a representative from Sony's device division would regularly visit Nintendo's headquarters in Kyoto to try to sell parts to Nintendo, but so far talks had not developed into a deal. During one of these visits to Kyoto, on April 15, 1986, Kutaragi accompanied the representative, planning to try to interest Nintendo in a joint venture with Sony. The Nintendo personnel whom they met showed an interest in Kutaragi's proposal, but the discussion went no further at the time.

Kutaragi knew that even his own company did not back the proposal. Some at Sony knew of his penchant for digital technology, but few supported his ideas for integrating this technology into product development. On the contrary, many saw him as a dangerous subversive who ignored the cornerstone of Sony's business at the time—analog video. Kutaragi explains, "I focused on Nintendo because I was convinced that the game machine would become the main home-use entertainment player in the future. But nobody in Sony agreed with me at the time. They all thought game machines were mere toys and not something Sony should make. Most engineers believed that the technology used in game machines was bound to be low-tech."

Kutaragi was desperate to create a framework that would enable Sony to make money from the explosion in information technology. To be successful in this field, a company needs to have a sound business model. However, Kutaragi was the only person in Sony at the time who thought this way. "It was hopeless trying to argue the importance of game machines at Sony. People with an old mind-set find it difficult to change their way of thinking. They thought it would take too long to start a new business from scratch with venture capital. So the only way to initiate change was from the outside. We could join forces with the best-performing company in the field. We would sell them our technology, establish a track record, and use that as the springboard to future success. That was my reasoning."

Kutaragi's initial approach to Nintendo did not lead to a business relationship, but Nintendo liked the next product he tried to sell them: the PCM (pulse coded modulation) sound generator system. Nintendo had been using an FM (frequency modulation) sound generator for the Famicom, and Kutaragi spent a lot of time persuading Nintendo's technical personnel to use PCM, which has a far better sound quality. At first, Nintendo was reluctant to switch to PCM because all existing Famicom software assets were FM-based.

PCM was superior to FM with respect to software flexibility as well; the PCM format held far greater potential for software innovation, a crucial factor in game-machine design.

Nintendo ultimately adopted Kutaragi's proposal, and this quickly led to a close relationship between the two companies.

THE FIRST PLAYSTATION PROJECT: THE DEFINITION OF LARGE-SCALE MEDIA VISION

The first joint project for the two companies was the PlayStation project. The name "PlayStation" was conceived in the process of joint development work with Nintendo. As Kutaragi says: "If a computer for work is a workstation, a computer for play is a 'playstation.' But in those days, nobody at Sony could understand such a concept."

Sony's fortunes were always foremost in Kutaragi's mind when he worked, and he saw an alliance with Nintendo as a way to demonstrate the importance of game machines to the future of the company. He thought of PlayStation as the ideal opportunity for Sony to utilize technology in the field of computer games.

As an interim measure, Kutaragi thought of the CD. More than five years had passed since Sony and Philips had developed and released the CD. There were many CD players on the market worldwide, and portable CD players (such as the Sony Discman) were a fast-growing market. The original PlayStation concept came from the idea of linking the CD player with the Super Famicom. Kutaragi thought that the formula "Super Famicom + CD = PlayStation" would be ideal for the Sony-Nintendo partnership.

In October 1989, a few Sony engineers began design work on PlayStation. Kutaragi made the following entries in his business reports at the time, expressing his ideas and strategic thinking about the game machine:

- August 1989 business report: "Planning a fun computer that links an AI function with the sound input/output interface. We want to create an 'intelligent pet.'"
- September 1989 business report: "We're developing the PlayStation. Planning a system aimed at junior and senior high school students that represents a fusion of games, electronic musical instruments, music, audiovisual technology, and stationery. Aiming to make sufficient impact on the market by selling three million units in the first year. The means to this end is the Super Famicom. Will further clarify the concept as things progress."
- October 1989 business report: "Creating a new framework that combines the world of Super Famicom games and digi-

tal audio technology. The game machine will be transformed into a high-tech tool that can process data in any way desired."

- November 1989 business report: "PlayStation will be positioned as the future mainstay digital product and a step towards introducing computers into the home. Together with Nintendo, we will create infrastructure for a home-use computer. This will effectively link game machines with Sony's audiovisual technology. We are not aiming for a one-way audiovisual player, but want to develop the product as a system. Strategically speaking, the first step is to increase computer penetration centered on Nintendo game machines. The second step is fusion of game machines with the many CD and LD players currently on the market. After that, we will look at third-party optical disk publishing and education businesses, and establish CD as a medium. The technical infrastructure is already in place with the Sony/Philips input/output terminal. This is the optical digital output."

In 1989, Kutaragi's vision was extraordinarily forward-thinking. It went far beyond the still-unrealized Sony-Nintendo CD-compatible game machine (the first-generation PlayStation), and even future versions of the Sony PlayStation. What Kutaragi envisioned even at that time was the PlayStation as it is destined to become. The current PlayStation, a specialist game platform, is only one aspect of a more elaborate system which he set out to develop. Moreover, it was grounded in the themes of using Sony resources and creating a system rather than a single product.

Particularly significant is the entry in the November 1989 business report describing the first step as a joint project with Nintendo and the second step as the development of third-party publishing and education businesses. This is nothing if not a description of today's PlayStation.

A prototype was developed along these lines. The development contract with Nintendo was signed on January 1, 1989.

The contract bore the signatures of Norio Ohga, president of Sony, and Hiroshi Yamauchi, president of Nintendo.

The initial idea was to connect a CD player to the Super Famicom using an external digital interface, but the specifications were later changed to include a built-in CD-ROM drive. A built-in drive was favored because connecting separate units with a cable was inelegant and, more important, would be inconvenient for the user. Indeed, the Famicom already had the Disk System™, which called for complex wiring. The developers also learned from the experience of Sharp's Twin Famicom, which had a built-in disk system and sold quite well. Already, CD-ROM drives were becoming quite affordable.

Eventually, Sony and Nintendo agreed that Sony would produce a game machine with a built-in CD-ROM drive, and Nintendo would produce a CD-ROM adapter for connecting a drive to the Super Famicom. On May 29, a design prototype slightly larger than the Super Famicom, with a built-in CD-ROM drive, was completed. It had a front-loading mechanism just like a CD player; a tray would come out when a button was pressed and would wait for the CD to be loaded. It was a white, smart-looking mock-up with fashionable styling typical of Sony products.

On October 29, 1990, several engineers, including Kutaragi, the new media team, and the computer graphics production team from Epic/Sony Records, met in Aoyama. Epic/Sony was moving to Akasaka, so Kutaragi and his team would occupy the space it had vacated. They began steadily working on hardware and software development. Seven months later came word of the deal between Nintendo and Philips.

NINTENDO'S BETRAYAL

The Consumer Electronics Show in Chicago in the summer of 1991 brought bedlam for Sony. Although Sony had been horrified at suddenly being dumped in favor of Philips and struggled to find an appropriate response, the company president had decided to proceed with the presentation of its new product. On June 1, the day of the announcement, Olaf Olafsson, president of Sony Electronic Publishing, a subsidiary of Sony America that produced game software, unveiled the new game machine with a built-in CD-ROM drive. He declared with great confidence: "Sony will throw open its doors to software makers to produce software utilizing music and movie assets." Sony was the focus of considerable attention that day.

Nintendo's announcement was made the following day. The assembled reporters were expecting to hear the details behind Sony's announcement, so they were dumbfounded to hear that Nintendo would form an alliance with Philips, not Sony, to produce an extended-function CD-ROM system. In the view of many in the media, Sony had been utterly humiliated.

Ohga's fury was intense. "How dare they tear up a contract that I signed?" he raged. But there was nothing Sony could do. Ohga placed a telephone call to Jan Timmer, then head of Philips' Home Appliance Division, which yielded no results. Sony quickly formed a project team, called CMG (for crisis management group), to deal with the situation. Nobuyuki Idei, Teruhisa Tokunaka (today president of Sony Computer Entertainment, Inc., or SCEI), and members of the contract, external relations, legal, and public relations departments discussed the situation for several days, but they could not come up with asolution.

A management meeting on July 2 concluded with the decision to prepare quickly for litigation. "One more thing," said Ohga at the end of the meeting. "We will never withdraw from this business. Keep going!"

Computers were the only product area in which Sony did not enjoy commercial success. Its home computer, the MSX, had suffered numerous setbacks, and its Quarter-L PC was not selling well. Although its NEWS workstation had made a promising start, it later proved to be a disappointment. Still, Ohga did not want to let the light of Sony's computer business go out.

Nintendo was also in a precarious spot. It had turned the tables on Sony, fully aware of the risk it was taking. If Sony stopped supplying the sound chip for the Super Famicom, which was selling extremely well, because of Nintendo's breach of contract, its business would suffer badly. Nintendo did not think that Sony would be brave enough to take such a step. They were right. As an original equipment manufacturer (OEM), Sony was obliged to fulfill its responsibility of supplying the part. Although it is true that some at Sony urged halting supply of the part, supplying the part and the breach of contract were separate issues. Sony decided to deal with each issue separately; it continued to supply the sound chip and decided not to take Nintendo to court. However, Sony's indecisive posture at the time would lead to a drawn-out resolution of the situation.

As Sony prepared for volume production of the new product, negotiations with Nintendo were deadlocked. Nintendo asserted that Sony should stick to nongame areas. But how could a distinction be made between game and nongame software? Nintendo was obviously attempting to wear Sony down, but Sony took Nintendo's actions at face value and became entangled in fruitless talks.

Although some people at Sony criticized the decision to continue with the talks, negotiations continued into 1992. Many in the company were still opposed to the idea of Sony's involvement in the computer games market, and they resented Kutaragi for having gotten Sony involved in this mess with Nintendo. Many tried to sabotage his plans. Business reports written by Kutaragi at the time reveal his feelings as a party to the conflict:

- January 1992 business report: "It was a year of many complications. After endless negotiations, both companies agreed to make their products mutually compatible. But there is no consensus within Sony about why we are engaged in this business. We are wasting time and missing opportunities while expecting too much from Nintendo and dealing with them in blind good faith."

Kutaragi's reports the following month also document his frustration and exhaustion. His bitterness is almost palpable, but there is a noticeable change in his point of view:

- February 1992 business report: "The industry is at a watershed. Nintendo's superiority is crumbling. It has become obvious that Nintendo no longer deserves to be Sony's partner. Sony should go its own way."

Kutaragi was starting to think that Sony had to be self-reliant and set its own pace. There was no shortage of evidence to support his decision. A morning paper reported on March 3, 1992, that the consumer electronics giant Matsushita Electric would enter the 3-DO market. Furthermore, by then it had become obvious that the reported joint project between Nintendo and Philips had been a mere ploy. Knowing it must take decisive action, Sony terminated all talks with Nintendo on May 6, 1992.

OHGA FACES A DECISION: THE PATH TO "DO IT!"

Many at Sony were appalled by the Nintendo fiasco and wanted no further involvement with the game business. For his part, Kutaragi was convinced that the company must not retreat from the business and should develop CD-ROM game machines independently.

Teruhisa Tokunaka, a member of the crisis management group, describes Kutaragi's stance at the time: "When the joint project with Nintendo finally collapsed, Kutaragi was obviously shaken. He would get depressed or angry. But it seemed to me that his dream was unchanged. So I said to him, 'If you really want to do this, do it on your own terms, not somebody else's.' He said he wanted to think about it, and went off. About a month later, he showed me a piece of paper with his idea on it, saying this is what he wanted to do. The idea was outstanding: a 3-D computer graphics 'playstation,' not a workstation. Moreover, the price would be as low as possible so it would be accessible to everyone, yet it would employ highly advanced technology. 'This is great!' I thought."

The question was: How could the project be kept alive? Kutaragi had been pushed into similar situations in the past, most notably with the two-inch floppy disk and the development of the LCD television soon after he joined the company. But the CD-ROM game-machine project put Kutaragi's whole career as a Sony engineer at stake.

The management meeting on June 24, 1992, was critical. The fate of the project would be decided at the meeting, which was chaired by Sony president Ohga. The situation seemed hopeless. Nearly everyone present argued that Sony should pull out of the games market. Kutaragi thought the situation had reached a critical juncture and said: "Having listened to what everyone is saying, I can see three options. First, to continue indefinitely with the traditional, Nintendo-compatible 16-bit game machines. Second, to sell game machines in a format proprietary to Sony. Third, to retreat from the market. I believe Sony should choose the second option of selling proprietary-format machines."

"What reasons do you have to justify pursuing that option?" Ohga demanded.

As if on cue, Kutaragi explained, "We've been secretly developing a new format using 3-D computer graphics separately from the Nintendo-compatible machine. Using this technology, we can produce astounding 3-D graphics that the Super Famicom can't hope to compete with."

"What scale of LSI chip do you need?"

"In terms of gate arrays, about one million."

"What? A million gates?"

"We already have a basic design concept, though it's still at the architecture stage."

Suddenly, Ohga burst out laughing. Kutaragi had shaken Ohga's composure by citing a figure beyond his comprehension. "You're dreaming! A million gates is impossible! The best we could do is twenty to thirty thousand, a hundred thousand at most." Ohga's estimate was based on figures he had heard from Sony's semiconductor division. With Sony's capabilities at the time, the best LSI chip it could hope to build was one with 100,000 gates.

But having done his own research, Kutaragi knew that the figure of one million gates would soon be an achievable target in the industry. "It's by no means impossible to integrate one million gates on an LSI chip. Unless we can do that, we can't produce three-dimensional computer graphics. Are you just going to sit back and accept what Nintendo did to us?" He appealed intensely and repeatedly to Ohga in this manner, provoking the Sony president. Finally, having reignited Ohga's rage against Nintendo and stirred up his emotions, Kutaragi demanded: "Please make a decision!"

Unable to control his fury, Ohga replied, "If you really mean it, prove to me that it's possible." Then he formed a fist, pounded on the desk, and shouted: "DO IT!"

Then, a bit more calmly, Ohga said, "There's no hope of making further progress with a Nintendo-compatible 16-bit machine. Let's chart our own course." Had he taken the time to think about the situation more thoroughly, he surely must have concluded that the risks of such an action were too great. But in the heat of the moment, he could not suppress his desire to see Sony succeed independently.

KUTARAGI'S CONFIDENCE

Kutaragi was certainly not bluffing at the meeting. During the long days of the dispute with Nintendo, he had secretly instructed his subordinates to select a CPU and work on developing computer graphics technology. Kutaragi himself had been working on the legal aspects of the Nintendo problem and had no time to work on the project.

Around that time, Sony's general research laboratory, NEWS workstation team, and semiconductor division had started working independently on computer graphics technology. Kutaragi brought these engineers together into a study group devoted to the "graphics synthesizer," the key concept of the PlayStation. Although Kutaragi called it "Sony's own format," in fact the technology had a diverse pedigree.

Kutaragi wrote the following in his May 1992 business report: "On the subject of developing the next-generation game machine. It is based on the development of component technologies of virtual reality. We need to develop spatial technology that will turn two-dimensional sprite functions into 3-D. We also need to develop a real-time, three-dimensional computer graphics engine and texture-mapping technology. In this way, we can integrate two-dimensional and three-dimensional technologies." Clearly, Kutaragi hoped to develop a game-machine format proprietary to Sony.

Kutaragi's confidence was based on his faith in 3-D technology. After his encounter with System G, he had vigorously explored the field of computer graphics, which he loved as a hobby as well as a professional interest. By taking the initiative to immerse himself in the world of computer graphics, he was able to chart a new course for computer games. "We made a thorough attempt to simulate the content we could express using CD-ROM. Graphic representation in game software at the time was two-dimensional, like Super Mario and Dragon Quest. From the mid-1980s, when I first saw System G, I dreamed of the day when 3-D computer graphics could be enjoyed at home. What kind of graphics could we create if we combined a real-time, 3-D computer graphics engine with CD-ROM? Surely this would develop into a new form of entertainment."

Computer graphics artists were in an unfortunate position. There were some one hundred of them in Japan at the time, and Kutaragi was in contact with about twenty of them. Most of them longed to make movies using computer graphics, but this was simply not possible with the technology available in the early 1990s. Many of them made TV commercials instead, dreaming of winning the Grand Prix, an award conferred by *Pixel*, a computer graphics trade publication.

Once, upon meeting one of these artists, Kutaragi said, "In the near future, computer games will incorporate computer graphics." "Is that true?" asked the artist, his eyes sparkling with delight. Over drinks, both men indulged in speculation about the future of computer graphics and the things they would like to achieve using this technology. Kutaragi says, "Meeting with these top artists formed the foundation of a very important idea for the future PlayStation."

Partly as a result of suh encounters, Kutaragi was able to formulate a precise idea of how he could use 3-D technology strategically. It was rumored that Sega's next-generation game machine would feature 3-D graphics, which to him made Sony's exploring 3-D technology and taking the lead in the game-machine industry an unavoidable course of action. If Sony could bring about a major paradigm shift from two- to three-dimensional games, it would enjoy an enviable position in the industry. The Nintendo fiasco only fueled Kutagari's resolve: "We ended up having problems because we tried to work with another company. It would be better to put the same effort into creating a 3-D world of our own."

"DO WHATEVER IT TAKES TO PRODUCE THIS GAME MACHINE"

Ohga bears no hard feelings about the time his emotions were taken advantage of. On the contrary, he smiles when he recalls how Kutaragi pulled it off. "There is no doubt that Nintendo propelled Kutaragi in that direction," he says. "That incident was a formidable driving force. No doubt Nintendo had no idea Sony would go so far. My own anger at being stabbed in the back also provided impetus.

"I felt extraordinary determination. I was impressed by Kutaragi's idea and felt determined that this business must succeed. This was not a mere game machine, but a graphics computer. It is on a totally different level from Nintendo's game machines. I wanted to push the idea of selling something that would have cost tens of millions of yen some years ago for just tens of thousands of yen. Also, Sony had failed with all its computer initiatives, going back to MSX. I wanted to establish a core business other than audiovisual equipment. As the chief executive, I wanted to be Kutaragi's strongest supporter."

Executive decisions cannot be made based simply on a business plan. A decision as to whether a project will proceed should involve evaluating the person who will implement the project. Ohga not only saw the potential of Kutaragi's idea but believed in the man himself.

During the project period, Ohga consistently supported Kutaragi, even when there were strong views in Sony that the company should not be involved in game machines. Says Shigeo

Maruyama, currently vice chairman of SCEI and president of Sony Music Entertainment (SME): "President Ohga never said we should stop developing game machines. The person who made the real decision was President Ohga. In Kutaragi's case, it was determination rather than a decision. And after all, he is just an engineer."

There is no shortage of anecdotes illustrating Ohga's commitment to the PlayStation. One involves how Ohga himself took on the task of securing memory for the PlayStation, showing admirable courage in the process. For a year after the PlayStation went on sale, it was very difficult to get hold of memory chips. The success of Windows meant that memory supply was tight worldwide. Ohga made use of his contacts in the electronics industry and telephoned various semiconductor manufacturers. "Our order was so huge that a managing director of the supplier came to see me at Sony," Ohga recalls. "He told me that the order for memory for the PlayStation accounted for 33 percent of the company's total production. 'We are delighted to receive such a large order,' he said, 'but if by chance the order has to be canceled, the impact on our business would be catastrophic. We therefore ask your company to guarantee the order.' I replied that the company could not guarantee it but that I would do so personally."

But Ohga's enthusiasm was not shared by all Sony employees, many of whom still wondered why a firm with world-class status should stoop to making game machines. Sony could remain a principal player in the audiovisual industry, the thinking went, where competitors were familiar with one another and where business negotiations were conducted in a civilized manner. The game-machine industry was simply too different culturally, and there was no need for Sony to enter that fray.

KEEPING THE PROJECT ALIVE: SEPARATION FROM SONY

There is no doubt that Ohga's support was a major factor in the success of PlayStation. "Kutaragi is far too talented," says the Sony president. "He had clashed with so many people that there was too much friction within the company; wherever he was, he was opposed and found fault with by everyone. I could see that his views would be crushed at Sony headquarters. If I kept such a talented employee at Gotanda, I knew he would never make it.

"So I took Kutaragi and nine of his team to Sony Music, cleared the former office of Epic Sony in Aoyama, and set up an environment where Kutaragi's team could develop the CD-ROM with software staff. Although many people complained at Sony about this decision, I went ahead with it regardless. I can say with confidence that one of the factors that led to the success of the PlayStation was removing the genius Kutaragi from Sony."

Kutaragi first visited the Epic Sony office in the Shin-Aoyama Building, Aoyama 1-chome, Tokyo, on April 6, 1989. The circuit board prototype for the Super Famicom sound generator chip had just been completed. Function tests had gone well, and Kutaragi was feeling very relieved. He decided to pay a visit to Epic Sony. He had heard that Epic Sony was an interesting company with tremendous vitality, due in no small measure to an outstanding producer there named Maruyama.

Most people believed that game machines like the Famicom were little more than a collection of basic technologies, and that the technology for even the next generation of Famicom would be nothing out of the ordinary. It was out of the question to talk to anyone about the secret joint development work with Nintendo, or about the content of the project. It was frustrating for Kutaragi not to be able to talk to anyone about working on such advanced technology.

Kutaragi happened to hear that there was a team at Epic Sony that developed Famicom software. This was Maruyama's organization. Yuji Takahashi, who is now an executive director of Polydor, was also a member of the team, and later went on to take sole charge of negotiations with third-party software companies. Kutaragi made his way from Gotanda to Aoyama with the belief that Takahashi would understand the importance of game machines. Of course, at the time he had no idea that he would end up being based in Aoyama. He recalls, "Compared with the stuffiness of Sony headquarters, Epic Sony at Aoyama seemed like utopia. I met Mr. Maruyama and thought that he was a businessman truly capable of creative management. I decided that if anything happened at Sony, I would go to work for him."

Sony is a serious-minded company. It makes products meticulously, and markets and distributes them properly. Although the outside world perceives Sony as a free and liberal company, it could not survive if that were so. As a manufacturer, it needs a proper order and organizational hierarchy. Software companies tend to have more freedom and do not have such a rigid order.

Epic Sony was established in 1978 as a CBS Sony spin-off. A decade later, it was going from strength to strength. The label's top artists included The Chanels, Misato Watanabe, Motoharu Sano, and TN Network, and it was highly successful. Maruyama played a leading role in the company's success. He was not actually working as a producer, but was a managing producer who had other producers working for him. In other words, he was a manager who nurtured producers, who nurtured artists. This is what Kutaragi meant by "a businessman capable of creative management."

Although he is now president of Sony Music, Maruyama has changed very little. He wears a white polo shirt, a navy jacket, jeans, and sneakers. The rumor that he leaves the office every night for small live-music venues nationwide is true. "It was a five-year struggle after founding Epic Sony, but around the time Kutaragi came to visit us, we had acquired a method-ology of how to produce a music hit," Maruyama says. "Although I was just a salaried employee of Sony Music, I did what I liked as a top manager of a company. I didn't have to report to my boss and could make my own decisions, so it was great fun."

Lyricist Kotaro Asao describes the atmosphere of Epic Sony at the time: "In those days, Epic Sony didn't have any artists. At lunchtime, everyone was having fun playing cards. It was like a university club and seemed very relaxed. Other record companies were full of older, experienced people and had a very strong record industry atmosphere, but somehow Epic Sony was totally different. I would visit for a cup of tea, with no reason to go there for work. I would sit at a desk that wasn't occupied and talk to people about movies or whatever, and on each occasion I would have an incredibly good time. Everyone was pleasant, and since there wasn't much urgent work, they were all free from pressure and stress. When every-one was in the office and having fun, a gray-haired fellow from Shonan [a casual seaside resort near Tokyo] would turn up, say-ing something like 'Hey, guys, I've got tickets for a ball game at Jingu Stadium tonight.' For a long time, his identity had been one of the seven mysteries of Epic Sony. We had no idea that this man would become the chief executive of Sony Music."

Kutaragi told Maruyama everything: that he was making a dig-ital sound generator IC at Sony; that it was for the Nintendo Super Famicom; how digital engineers were not appreciated at Sony; how he wanted to make a 3-D computer graphics game machine in the future. It didn't take long for Kutaragi and

Maruyama to hit it off. Kutaragi would always find some excuse to visit Aoyama and talk at length with Maruyama and his team.

"Looking back," recalls Maruyama, "Kutaragi didn't say much to me about how badly he was being treated at Sony. The only thing he mentioned was that he was clashing with the Sony CD/I group. I told him that although CD/I was involved, I would support him. [At the time, Sony Music was also engaged in the CD/I business.] I felt I should support him, because what he was doing made sense. I realized how reckless Kutaragi was only after we became colleagues and were working together on the PlayStation."

Maruyama had a reason for welcoming this intruder. He had first encountered the Famicom at a publishing company party in 1984, the year after the game machine first went on sale. He had expected it to be something simple, like a tennis game, but he soon became engrossed. "I was hooked. People in the music business love games. Waiting rooms of recording studios always provide game machines. Musicians waiting to go on would improve their skills as they killed time playing Pacman and Space Invaders. That night, when I couldn't stop playing the Famicom, I was convinced that game machines would become a powerful rival of records. We could either destroy them or grab a share of the pie. So I said to Mr. Ohga that we, too, should make game software. In a few years' time, Epic Sony set up a new media office."

Unfortunately, the new business flopped. By then the Super Famicom had come along, and Epic Sony could only produce software that imitated rival products. They could not compete with software makers that had spent years acquiring the expertise to create special effects. "The truth is, all the games we made were dismissed by Kutaragi as garbage," says Maruyuma. "We were desperate; something had to be done. If

Kutaragi and I have something in common, it's the fact that we're both outsiders. In those days, Epic Sony software wasn't officially accepted by Sony Music headquarters, merely tolerated. Kutaragi was working on the joint project with Nintendo, going against the CD/I, which was mainstream at Sony. I suppose we were both hungry for success. But we both had our pride."

Maruyama wanted to create an innovative game, but he did not have the technology to achieve it. Kutaragi had the technology for a game machine, but not the skill to produce game software. "I decided that my business would not succeed unless I could motivate Kutaragi," says Maruyama. He therefore supported Kutaragi both overtly and behind the scenes. He allowed Sony's Kutaragi to hang out at Epic Sony and decided to begin development of CD-ROM software for the Super Famicom. "I did this to help Kutaragi. At the time, we were aiming to produce ten titles. We worked hard at it, but in the end the project was canceled and we lost $7 million to $8 million."

During the Nintendo crisis, some had suggested that Nintendo should produce the games for the compatible machines and Sony should produce other software. "My response was that Sony should split with Nintendo and go its own way," says Maruyama. "I told President Ohga through President Toshio Ozawa [then president of Sony Music] that there would be trouble if we didn't do it on our own. I said that the format shouldn't be shared with another company, and that we had to secure it for ourselves."

Why was it important to gain control of the format? "Having your own format gives you all kinds of information," says Maruyama. "You learn a great deal from analyzing all this information in various ways and verifying and comparing the results. In this way, your business activities become more objective and universal."

One of Maruyama's roles was to act as a pipeline between Kutaragi and Ohga. Since Kutaragi was just an ordinary employee, it was difficult for him to meet directly with Ohga. He would have to set up an appointment through his superior, who would have to go through Ohga's secretary. Many days would pass before the meeting could take place. "So Kutaragi thought of using me. He was an expert in the way he made use of me," says Maruyama.

Ohga and Maruyama were both founding members of CBS Sony. Ohga knew the employees of CBS Sony well in the early years—"until they grew to reach one hundred employees," says Ohga. Maruyama, whose given name is Shigeo, was called "Shige" by Ohga. If Maruyama phoned Ohga's secretary, it was indeed a hot line to Ohga.

Although officially Maruyama should have gone through President Ozawa of Sony Music, Ozawa said, "If that's what it's about, why don't you phone Mr. Ohga yourself?" Although few people at Sony could persuade Ohga, those at Sony Music could speak their minds directly. Maruyama said to Ohga: "He's set his heart on doing this project. Why don't you let him work on it for a while?" Ohga's reply: "All right. I'll send him to you."

MAKING FULL USE OF SONY'S RESOURCES

Gaining the help of Maruyama, a software management expert, was a big step forward for Kutaragi. His next objective was to make use of Sony's resources. He believed the quickest way to a speedy start-up of his project was to make use of Sony's manpower, equipment, and financial resources. He knew that he was fortunate in this respect, because if he were to try to set up a venture business outside the company, he would have to start from scratch.

Since he did not enjoy much credibility at Sony, however, he knew he couldn't ask for these resources himself. His strategy, therefore, was to have a key person—someone who was trusted by top management, had a successful career at Sony headquarters, and came into contact with the top brass on a daily basis—serve as an intermediary. The person Kutaragi selected was Teruhisa Tokunaka, with whom he had worked in the crisis management group during the Nintendo incident.

Tokunaka was a highly respected member of the Sony headquarters team that had worked on the acquisition of Sony Music and Sony Pictures. Kutaragi first consulted Ohga about his choice. Ohga replied, "That's a great idea. He'll be good," then immediately backed his words with action and made the necessary arrangements. "Tokunaka functions as an anchor," Ohga explained. "Left to himself, there is no telling what excesses Kutaragi might commit. That's why we asked Tokunaka to keep him firmly in line."

Tokunaka had met Kutaragi in 1988, at a meeting in which the consequences of the proliferation of CD formats was discussed. "Kutaragi looked grumpy and didn't say a word," say Tokunaka. "It was then that I learned about the first PlayStation project. I didn't understand everything that was said at the meeting, because it was the first time I had heard about the subject, but I think it was decided that Kutaragi's wish to work on the PlayStation independently from Sony was acceptable."

Tokunaka joined Sony in 1969. While training at the company's legal department on a temporary assignment, he read a memo that was left lying on the desk of Tamotsu Iba (today vice president of Sony), who was manager of the department at the time. It had a huge impact on him. "I was amazed that there were such gifted people in the world. It was a memo about Sony's strategy, and I wanted to become someone who could write like this. That's why I asked to be assigned to the legal department," recalls Tokunaka.

He was officially assigned to the Sony legal department in 1971, and immediately began work on a U.S. antitrust law court case. During his two-and-a-half-year stay in the United States, he learned the ins and outs of M&A. Then he returned to Japan and worked in the planning department of Sony's domestic sales division before moving to the corporate planning office, consolidating the market position of Sony's 8mm video.

At the time, Sony was stung by the failure of Betamax and saw the 8mm video as a product to compete against VHS, but Tokunaka disagreed with the policy, arguing that instead of competing with VHS, Sony should utilize 8mm video as a portable format. Consequently, the 8mm format became a world leader in the camcorder market.

Next he worked on the Tokyo side of the acquisition of Columbia Records of Sony in the United States. "I had experience with M and A from early in my career, so I knew all about the process." When Kutaragi selected Tokunaka to help him, Tokunaka was on assignment in the States. Leaving his family behind, he had gone to New York to prepare for the possibility of Sony's moving its overseas division headquarters to New York. "Kutaragi would phone me in New York in the middle of the night. He would wake me up and say, 'The project I'm working on isn't making any progress. What can I do? Do you have any ideas?' Once Kutaragi made up his mind, he took no notice of the time difference."

Then Tokunaka was ordered to return to Japan. His U.S. posting, which was supposed to last eighteen months, had ended after only nine. He returned home in May 1993 and was immediately appointed manager of the SCEI Establishment Preparation Office. Ohga said to him, "Make a business plan for the PlayStation as quickly as possible. Finish it by July."

THREE SCENARIOS

There were countless things to do. Tokunaga's view on the hardware for the new game machine was "I wasn't worried, because I was certain Kutaragi would come up with something good." He was more concerned about the counterattack expected from competitors after the PlayStation went on sale. Launching such an advanced product meant that PlayStation would initially take the lead in the market. Competitors would not stand idle; they would immediately attempt to develop and market better-performing, more attractive game machines. Could Sony withstand this response, and how would it prepare for future offensives?

Tokunaga could have left all this to Kutaragi, but there were too many imponderables in Kutaragi's business plan. The main question was whether software makers would produce software for PlayStation. At the time, retail and distribution of game software was dominated by the Shoshinkai (today known as Isshinkai), a group of some fifty wholesalers organized by Nintendo. How and through whom could Sony sell its software under those circumstances? What about pricing? What software should be offered? What selling structure should the company use? How about royalties? Sony had to start from scratch in all these areas.

Only one thing was certain at this point: The game machine would bear the name "PlayStation." Everyone at Sony agreed that the name used in the CD-ROM project with Nintendo should be kept. The code name for the project was PS/X.

When formulating strategy, Kutaragi's team was guided by one concern: How could it gain the support of the user? "It was simple, really," says Tokunaka. "If software developers supported us—that is, accepted the PlayStation as a platform— we would go ahead with the business. Otherwise, we wouldn't. That was the bottom line."

Tokunaka says the strategy for wooing software producers followed logically from there: "First, produce a format that creators find attractive; make it a format that motivates them. Second, propose a business structure that motivates business managers: the license or royalty system. Third, if software developers show an interest in our proposal, develop a distribution structure based on that. We did hundreds of simulations."

This took until July 20, 1993. Next, a meeting to discuss the PS/X business plan took place, with Ohga in attendance. During the meeting, Tokunaka detailed the prospects for the PS/X as follows: "There are three scenarios—call them A, B, and C. A is the positive scenario, with an established format and a strong business environment. B is less positive; the PS/X is initially a hit, but long-term success is uncertain. C is that although the PS/X does well to start with, we eventually have to withdraw from the market. Although I would like to feel confident of victory, it is an extremely competitive market and it would not be realistic to expect a huge success. The most likely scenario is somewhere between A and B. If we get that far, the start-up would be considered a success. We're looking at a time span of two to three years."

Ohga remained deep in thought before saying with a nod, "Right, let's go ahead on that." Then he added, "As far as the user is concerned, it doesn't matter whether the medium is CD or CD-ROM. The point is that children enjoy it. The deciding factor will be the attractiveness of the software produced by the software houses. I want them to create software with imaginative screens, full of ideas, and content that's really fun to play."

What was to be the business result of PlayStation, launched eighteen months later? Was it Scenario A, B, or C?

DECEMBER 3, 1994: THE FIRST 100,000 UNITS DISAPPEAR

December 3, 1994, was a watershed in the history of the game-machine industry. PlayStation, Sony's next-generation game machine, went on sale that day. In Akihabara, Tokyo, several hundred people were lined up outside a store selling the PlayStation when the store opened; some had been camped out all night. Many stores were sold out of the game machine before noon and desperately tried to order more from SCEI.

Sports Nippon reported on December 4, 1994: "A 30-year-old Tokyo man who does temporary work was at the head of the line. He said, 'I got here at 8:00 P.M. yesterday. It's [PlayStation] so utterly different from traditional game machines that I didn't even think about the price.'" The *Nihon Keizai Shimbun* reported on the same day, "About seven hundred people lined up outside the Laox Computer Game Store in Akihabara, Tokyo, which does not take advance orders. Some stayed up all night. Joshin Electric, a Kansai-based retailer, sold the PlayStation at seventy outlets (about half the company's total number of outlets), and most of them were sold out before noon."

Masashi Saeki (today manager of the PR Department at SCEI), who coordinated public relations at SCEI, went to the west exit of Shinjuku Station at 8:30 A.M. to see what was going on. He was certain that there would be a line of people outside the shuttered entrance of Yodobashi Camera, but all he saw were a few crows. He was looking in the wrong place. Yodobashi Camera had anticipated a mob scene and had set up a special sales area for the PlayStation around the corner from the main store. Saeki went there to find several hundred people standing in line. He was so delighted that he simply started to walk to the head of the long line.

On his way back, he thought he would speak to some of the people who had actually bought the machines, and he approached a youth of senior high school age. The boy looked startled and ran off. Suddenly, Saeki realized why: Dragon Quest had been making the headlines recently. Someone had accosted a person who had bought the highly popular game software and stolen it. The boy had mistaken him for a Dragon Quest thief! After the same thing happened two or three times, Saeki changed tactics. He spoke loudly when he came within three meters of the next person he decided to question: "Hello, I'm from Sony Computers. Could I please ask you some questions?"

The person stopped.

"What software did you buy?" asked Saeki.

"Ridge Racer."

"How much did you pay?"

"Do you own a Sega Station?"

In the Shinjuku area, the stores selling PlayStation were sold out by 11:00 A.M. All the main shopping districts in Japan were having the same experience. One hundred thousand of Sony's initial production run of 300,000 units would be sold that day. Sony executives had expected that the PlayStation would sell well, but they could not be sure until the product actually hit the shelves. Naturally, they were delighted to hear that the machine was being received so enthusiastically.

At Akihabara, Kutaragi, wearing a PlayStation sweatshirt, took photographs of the long line of people outside the stores. Saeki was treated to a grilled beef dinner at Mansei. "December 3 was an extremely rewarding day," he says. "I had never been so lucky in my life, so I bought thirty lottery tickets for the first time. One of them won me three thousand yen. I have never been so fortunate, before or since."

At Sony, meanwhile, jubilation was mixed with desperation. Company executives were frantic, wondering how to produce enough units to meet the huge demand. Production had to be increased immediately, but the 200,000 units slated to be made in December could not be put on the market immediately. Ssome of the units had to be kept back for the Christmas rush coming soon.

Orders flooded in even from those who had been hostile to the idea of Sony selling game machines. Many Sony employees tried to use contacts to secure for themselves even one PlayStation. On December 20, the wife of one Sony director telephoned Ohga. "I would like to ask you a favor," she said. "I want to give my grandchild a PlayStation for Christmas, but all the stores are sold out till after Christmas. Is there any way you could find one for my grandchild, Mr. Ohga?" she pleaded. She had lined up outside a department store in Yokohama but had not been able to buy one. "I'll do what I can to get one for you," Ohga said. Although he had heard reports that the PlayStation was selling well from the very first day, he found it difficult to believe it was selling so fast. "The woman thanked me, saying her child would be so pleased. I can smile and tell you anecdotes like this because we succeeded, but it would have been dismal had we failed."

What had Kutaragi done between the day Ohga handed down his critical decision to proceed with the project and the day PlayStation was launched on its journey to the top of the game-machine market? What strategies had he put into play in the key areas of technology, marketing, production, and the sales system? That is the subject of the next chapter.

3

Appealing to the Software Developers

A common theme embraced by those involved in the PlayStation project was, in Maruyama's words, "Let's do what we can as latecomers—and what only latecomers can do." Sony was the last player to enter this highly competitive market. Its rivals Nintendo and Sega Enterprises were already enormously powerful in the field. If Sony was to survive in the market, it would have to defeat them. Maruyama summarized Sony's challenge this way: "First of all, we have to examine in fine detail what Nintendo is doing, and identify what software developers, distributors, and users find unsatisfactory about it. Then we need to devise ways to solve these problems, to be able to propose solutions."

Sony's strategy, then, was to identify its competitors' weaknesses and work out how to use them to its advantage, something that a latecomer to the market was uniquely positioned to do.

NO SONY-DEVELOPED SOFTWARE

For a video game platform to succeed, many conditions must be right; the most important is a plentiful supply of software for the format. How could Sony create such an environment? First, it should be reiterated that Sony had no software of its own and was totally dependent on third-party companies for software supply. This was a totally different position from that of Sony's competitor Sega, which had a versatile and well-equipped software-production division for its arcade games and could easily transfer products that had succeeded in game arcades to the Sega Saturn.

This was not possible with the PlayStation. Epic Sony's software-production team, led by Maruyama, was far too inadequate to the task. Hence, the PlayStation's fate would be determined by Sony's ability to gain the support of software developers. Third-party software developers do not participate in unsuccessful formats, and they constantly observe the market to see which formats are beating out the competition. They have a keen eye for business opportunities and are quick to invest only in winning formats.

How could Sony persuade these companies to participate in the PlayStation project? No amount of internal discussion could provide the answer to this question, so Sony decided to ask software companies directly. Over a three-month period starting in May 1993, a team consisting of Maruyama, Tokunaka, Akira Sato (today vice president of SCEI), Yuji Takahashi (today executive managing director of Polydor), and Kutaragi visited more than a hundred companies throughout Japan, from Hokkaido in the north to Kyushu in the south.

They asked to meet not only management but software creators as well. They went in with an optimistic two-stage strategy: First they would attract game creators with the PlayStation's technological appeal. Then the creators would put pressure on management and Sony would subsequently win the company over. However, Sony's plan to meet creators was usually foiled, because management would typically take the lead in the initial meeting and the creators remained in the background. Usually the reaction was "Sony shouldn't get involved with video games. We're telling you this for your own good." The technological superiority of the PlayStation was not easy to get across to executives.

Says Akira Sato, who was responsible for formulating the PlayStation marketing strategy: "Looking at the status quo, it was obvious that we were no match for Nintendo. We were asking software houses to participate knowing that they would refuse. When we asked them to join us, the software houses all said, '3-D computer graphics won't happen for another ten years. Only people who have no idea of the realities of software development would talk about programming games in computer programming language (C). The game industry is a rough-and-tumble business and no place for amateurs. If you get involved thinking there's easy money to be had, you'll be badly burned.' On reflection, I think their advice was well meant."

"GO AHEAD, PROVIDED YOU CAN SELL THREE MILLION": THE RATIONALE

On the morning of June 25, 1993, the Sony team visited a company we'll call Company A, a firm well known for its role-playing games (RPG). The Sony side concluded after the meeting that the company was not a candidate for inclusion in the first group of PlayStation software developers. The president of Company A said, "In the Japanese market we don't think we should participate in a platform unless hardware sales are a minimum of three million units. NEC and Sega both fail on this count. And even if the PlayStation did sell three million units, we wouldn't decide to go ahead until we determined how well it was competing against other formats."

Kutaragi and the team wrote in their report of the meeting: "No further action to be taken at this stage. We'll visit them again if the PlayStation sells three million units."

By that time, 8 million Super Famicom consoles had been sold, so sales of 3 million units was seen, with justification, as the absolute bottom line for a game platform. A hardware product was considered successful only if it sold rapidly during its first year on the market. Slow but steady sales was simply not good enough. Being overtaken by a competing platform would be enough to cause a product to fail to become a de facto standard. Software makers did not want to participate in a format unless it was going to be successful. Selling 3 million units of hardware was the clear benchmark of success they sought.

The same day, the team visited Company B, another leading RPG maker, whose reaction was the same: "We'll consider it if sales exceed three million units. We use big teams, so we won't participate in a format that can't support sales of more than one million units per title. A hardware sales figure of three million units is the minimum requirement, and the combined price of hardware and software must be under $300. Matsushita's 3-DO has exceptional specifications, but $700 is a ridiculous price. Sony's a well-respected brand, so you're onto a winner if you can sell the hardware for $250."

Again Kutaragi's team wrote in their report: "No further action to be taken at this stage. We'll visit again if the PlayStation sells three million units."

The benchmark approach to marketing was partly due to cultural factors. Western markets—the United States, for example—were able to support both the Nintendo 64 (N64) and PlayStation platforms, but the Japanese market would permit only one format to survive. Why was this so?

"You need a cultural anthropological perspective," says Yoji Haraguchi, a director of Namco and a games marketing specialist. "It's probably the difference between an agricultural people tied to the land and a hunting people who move from area to area in pursuit of prey. In the West, there is no problem with one person preferring the PlayStation while another person likes the N64. In Japan, everyone wants to follow their neighbors' example. Japanese feel secure if they have the same things as everyone else, but if they behave differently they are alienated and excluded from the group. You have to be an extremely brave boy to buy an N64 when all your classmates have PlayStations."

When executives at software houses said, "3-D computer graphics won't happen for another ten years," they were simply being realistic. It was commonly accepted in the industry that game manufacturers would not be able to easily and cost-effectively manipulate 3-D computer graphics for quite some time—let alone incorporate them into home-use game machines. At that time it cost 300,000 yen to produce an animated computer graphics image lasting one second.

Namco, for example, found it utterly inconceivable that 3-D computer graphics could soon make its way into the home market. They responded to Sony at their first meeting: "The PlayStation represents extremely advanced technology. We doubt that it can be applied to consumer equipment." Namco had been concentrating on computer graphics technology for years and had already incorporated real-time 3-D computer graphics into its arcade games. Namco's assertion that the PlayStation's technology could not be applied to consumer equipment showed their pride in their own research efforts. There were two R & D groups in Namco at the time, one working on home-use game software and the other on arcade machines, the latter by far the larger and more promising.

Namco's view of the home video game machine market was that it was extremely price sensitive. The Super Famicom sold for $160, and Namco believed that a game machine would not sell unless its recommended retail price was less than $398 and the actual selling price was below $300, however good its performance. At that time an arcade game machine incorporating computer graphics technology cost $18,000.

Kutaragi and his team nonetheless felt that they had gained valuable information: Many top managers had thoughtfully explained to them in detail and in layman's terms why this business was so difficult. They learned about the demanding conditions and problems unique to the business, such as the difficulty in returning products, high royalties, and the inability to supply repeat orders.

Says Managing Director Kazumi Kitagami of Konami: "Sony contacted us to request a meeting. SCEI had only just been established, so the request was made using Sony's name, but they wouldn't say what it was about—they just asked to see me. I was curious and agreed. Sony was represented by Mr. Tokunaka, Mr. Takahashi, Mr. Kutaragi, and Mr. Maruyama. I was the only one present from Konami. My understanding was that Sony had no experience in the games market, so as one with more experience I taught them about various aspects of the industry. I thought it was wise of them to be prepared to listen to what we wanted, an approach totally in contrast with Nintendo's attitude. Mr. Kutaragi often came to see me afterward, asking me how much hardware memory we wanted and what shape of controller would be suitable."

Kitagami is a seasoned veteran in the computer game industry. He started with the design of arcade game machines and considered entering the home-use hardware market in the late 1980s. "Unfortunately, it required a huge investment," he says, "so however many business simulations we conducted, the conclusion was always the same: Don't do it."

Having done much research, Kitagami was quite knowledgeable about the state of the industry, in which Nintendo was the de facto standard. "I told them that they must be prepared for a rough ride if they were to enter the industry. But I didn't tell them not to try."

The Sony side listened quietly to Kitagami's words. Kitagami recalls: "They told me later that when they left the meeting, they were all pretty out of sorts." The Sony team, however, were not content merely to listen to other people's views. They made efforts to utilize in their business plan what they had learned, however negative it may be. Says Tokunaka: "Even if a software maker advises you against entering the business, you can't just accede and pull out. What we need to do is to say 'This is the problem. How do we create the process that leads to a solution?'"

As they made the rounds of software houses the team began to identify those with an interest in 3-D computer graphics. The problem was how to attract their interest and bring them over to Sony's side. "A few understood what we were trying to do, but most were skeptical, saying it was impossible," Tokunaka says.

SEGA'S 3-D COMPUTER GRAPHICS: VIRTUA FIGHTER TURNS THE TIDE

Kutaragi and his team will never forget the events of August 26, 1993. The Sony side sat in a room in their office, located in Makuhari at the time, waiting for a meeting with Company C (well known for its combat games) scheduled for that afternoon. The meeting commenced at 2 P.M., but the mood was definitely strange. It was the team's second meeting with Company C, and what they were saying completely contradicted their words from the first meeting. Company C had said emphatically at the first meeting, "Does Sony really want to commit suicide with the game business? Ours is a 2-D-image culture; we have no interest in 3-D images. Worldwide hardware sales of—let's say three million units—would be a prerequisite for us to join forces with you."

Hearing these words, Kutaragi's team assumed that Company C would be unlikely to participate in the PlayStation platform. Company C had qualified the critical 3 million figure with the term "worldwide sales" because its mainstay, combat games, were sold all over the world. Sony's response was "Oh well, we'll visit them again when we've sold three million units." Company C, however, said it was still considering Sony's proposal, so a second meeting was arranged for August 26.

The day came. As at the previous meeting, a verbal description of the platform was followed by a video demonstration, but this time there were no questions about the hardware. The difference between 2-D and 3-D was not mentioned either. The questions all concerned other subjects, such as price, distribution, and marketing strategy. Company C went so far as to say, "There are many different formats out at the moment, but of all of them we are particularly interested in Sony's PS/X." This marked a total reversal of their previous attitude, which was that the minimum requirement for Sony was to sell 3 million hardware units. Company C was now taking a positive stance.

What had made them change their minds? "Sega's Virtua Fighter," one of them said. "It's awesome. We were amazed—computer graphics really move in 3-D!"

Sega had unveiled its arcade game Virtua Fighter at the Makuhari Game Show that day. The group from Company C had attended the game show in the morning and dropped in at the nearby Sony office that afternoon on the way back. They had been overwhelmed by Virtua Fighter. That the 3-D images of Virtua Fighter had been commercialized had made a tremendous impact on them.

A Company C executive telephoned Sony the following day: "We didn't have time to discuss this yesterday, but you might be able to develop PS/X as an arcade machine as well. We've been talking to various software makers, and they are all very positive about PS/X."

Virtua Fighter had quickly transformed software developers' attitude toward Sony. Before it was released, they had been unimpressed by Sony's demonstrations and remained skeptical about the seriousness of Sony's intentions. They all responded by reading from the same script: They would reconsider if Sony could sell 3 million units of hardware. But Virtua Fighter changed all that. Having seen 3-D images move before their eyes, software houses began to take PS/X seriously. Some even began to initiate contact with Sony, saying: "We understand that Sony is working on 3-D computer graphics. Could you tell us about it more detail?"

Says Tokunaka: "We can't thank Sega enough for the timing of Virtua Fighter's release. They proved at just the right time that it was possible to make games with 3-D images. From then on, the tide turned in our favor."

In technology, the tide was just beginning to shift from 2-D to 3-D. It was only a matter of time before a software house developed a 3-D arcade machine. Perhaps it is ironic that the company proved to be Sega, whose Sega Saturn was to become the PlayStation's main rival. At the time Virtua Fighter was released, however, Tokunaka's heart was full of gratitude toward Sega.

THE ASTONISHING DEMONSTRATION

Sony took a major step forward with the PlayStation project in the fall of 1993, announcing on October 27 that it would enter the game machine market and establish SCEI. The press release read: "On November 16 Sony and Sony Music Entertainment will establish Sony Computer Entertainment Inc. (SCEI) to develop and market home-use game machines and software and engage in licensing activities with software houses. Both Sony and Sony Music Entertainment will have equity in the new company. SCEI aims to create a new world of computer entertainment by offering next-generation, home-use game machines with ultra-high-speed computer graphics display functions characteristic of high-performance graphics workstations."

Without breaking stride, Sony held a demonstration session for software developers the following day. Tokunaka recalls: "Using the business cards we had collected on our travels, we telephoned software companies across the country one after another and invited them to Sony."

A prototype LSI circuit had been completed in early October. A system built with the prototype achieved real-time 3-D computer graphics movement, with a *Tyrannosaurus rex* roaring on the screen. Moreover, it was not a simple, wire-frame picture, but a realistic one created by texture mapping. The picture generated, using System G technology, was moving!

Full of confidence in the prototype, Kutaragi now felt he had to show it to software houses' engineers as well. A demonstration meeting was held at 10 A.M. on October 28 at the No. 10 Auditorium at the rear of Sony's headquarters in Gotenyama, Shinagawa, in Tokyo. Three hundred software engineers representing sixty companies were in attendance. Six prototypes were arranged against the wall of the huge venue, hidden from view by the white cloths draped over them.

The previous day, Tokunaka had asked Ohga to make a speech on this occasion, and Ohga, for whom this was a special project, had readily agreed. "Our format depends on the support of software companies like yours," he told his audience in Sony Auditorium. "At present it has no software at all. Please help us produce the software. We would very much appreciate your cooperation. Sony is going to approach this business very seriously."

In spite of Ohga's passion, the audience remained silent. The mood in the auditorium was one of coolness and detachment. The consensus seemed to be "Is Sony really serious? We won't decide whether to participate until we've seen the technology inside the machine."

Then Kutaragi quickly removed the white cloths and switched on the prototypes. A demonstration of the dinosaur image began, with fifty people standing around each of the six tables holding the prototypes. The demonstration went smoothly; the image was crystal clear. The texture-mapped 3-D *Tyrannosaurus rex* on the screen responded sensitively to the commands of the controller and roared, lifelike.

The audience stood as if transfixed. Half an hour into the demonstration, every engineer in the room was still staring at the screen. The tension was palpable. Eventually the demonstration ended and it was time for the audience to leave. The engineers left with stunned expressions on their faces, looking bewitched.

Kutaragi was troubled. "Why was there no reaction even though we showed them something that actually moved?" he said. In fact, the engineers had been in such a state of shock that words had failed them. They had never witnessed such impressive images. They had seen a demonstration using a very expensive Silicon Graphics system, but the images in the Sony demonstration were equally dynamic—if not more so. Although the proof was there before their eyes, they had difficulty comprehending that this technology would become part of a home-use game machine. "When I talked to them later on, they all said that it had come as such a surprise that they went into a state of shock," Kutaragi recalls.

Needless to say, game creators cannot make interesting games unless they are motivated. Kutaragi's strategy, which emphasized inspiring game creators, finally began to bear fruit at this point. Those who had seen the demonstration reported to their companies' presidents that they had seen something extraordinary. In the afternoon following that day's demonstration, SCEI's telephones started ringing constantly. The calls were from game companies asking to hear more details about the prototype. Each of the software makers that called had a reason for participating in the Sony format.

WHY NAMCO DECIDED TO PARTICIPATE

Namco was one of the first software makers that Sony wanted to have on its side. Incorporating 3-D computer graphics into home-use game machines would be a natural for Namco, since it had many years of experience with computer graphics technology for arcade machines. Kutaragi personally had met with Namco's computer graphics engineers several times.

During the first meeting, held June 18, 1993, Namco had said of the PlayStation technology: "We doubt it can be applied to consumer equipment." However, Namco had in no way tried to dissuade Sony from entering the game-machine market.

The third meeting, held at the Aoyama office on July 27, was so animated that it took the Sony side by surprise. Sony conducted a demonstration that day using overhead projection (OHP) and demo software. The demo video, used for the first time that day, featured pictures generated by the newly completed prototype board using polygons. The video had not been completed in time for the previous meeting. This was the basic form of the demo that later stunned the software makers assembled at the first technical demonstration, but it was enough to impress Namco, one of the leaders in 3-D computer graphics games. The demo showed a beautiful 3-D object moving smoothly, as well as the realistic image of the dinosaur.

After the demo, a Namco arcade game engineer responded: "This is remarkable. Very little surprises me; the only times I've been truly surprised were when the Famicom was released, when System 22 [Namco's 3-D game board for arcade games—the fastest in the world at the time] was completed—and now. Let's work together on this." He promptly fired off a series of requests, one of which involved overlays: "Can you overlay the screen twice? Overlays would considerably expand the range of expression. For example, you could create a dynamic effect of a large character hit by a bullet and bursting into flames."

A crucial factor with computer game graphics is the number of overlays that can be made in one-sixtieth of a second, the time it takes to compose one TV field. The request was evidence that Namco executives had had many in-depth discussions among themselves after the previous meeting.

Kutaragi replied: "Yes, of course. Two or more overlays are possible."

Another Namco engineer demanded, "We want enough power to move large characters." The characters of the Famicom and Super Famicom were 8 and 16 pixels, respectively, but Namco wanted the PlayStation's characters to be even bigger.

Namco had started using System 22—the next-generation 3-D computer graphics technology it had developed for arcade machines—and was in the process of developing Ridge Racer, a new game based on System 22. Ridge Racer was later transplanted to the PlayStation platform, contributing significantly to the success of the release of the original PlayStation.

"If Namco were to participate in PS/X, and if the technology could be applied to arcade games as well, we could avoid duplication of investment in development and reduce our costs," said Shigekazu Nakamura, Namco's senior managing director in charge of technology. Nakamura focused on the example of Capcom's Street Fighter, which was developed for arcade games and was easily adapted to the Super Famicom. "We would like to use PS/X for arcade games, even if it means having to stop all non–System 22 games. But for that, we'll need to reorganize," said Nakamura.

Namco had its own reasons for appreciating the PlayStation technology. It had started developing 3-D computer graphics technology in 1985. Says Nakamura: "Our goal was to differentiate ourselves in the arcade game market because 3-D would make an exponential difference to the expressive capability of 2-D images. But it was rather difficult with the technology available in those days. Nobody had any experience of

3-D computer graphics, so we all studied the subject as we started the research."

The only 3-D computer graphics available at the time were used in flight simulators. Applying the same technology to an arcade game would cost hundreds of thousands of dollars. The first 3-D computer graphics arcade game was Winning Run, which was released in 1989. It did not sell particularly well, however. The selling price was only about $10,000, which meant it was technically limited, and the technology available was still quite crude. Only 60,000 polygons per second could be generated, they could be filled in using single colors only, and movements were inconsistent because the program was limited in its ability to perform calculations. It was no match for the highly sophisticated 2-D images.

As time passed, however, creators became more skilled at using 3-D computer graphics and the performance of software steadily improved. For example, the 1991 version of Winning Run had the same number of polygons as the original version, but it was considerably faster.

Namco, like its rivals, was taken aback by Sega's Virtua Fighter. Sega, Namco's archrival in the arcade game machine market, had developed a 3-D combat game that turned people's heads. A new genre of 3-D computer graphics, a technology many had believed would not be commercialized until the next century, had made a bold appearance in the market for arcade game software. Says Namco Senior Managing Director Nakamura, "I felt we had to do this as well, and we had a fighting chance if we could develop an arcade machine based on the PlayStation." Here, too, Virtua Fighter provided the impetus for participation in the PlayStation project.

There were two main types of arcade machines: large machines that cost more than ¥1 million, which were composed of cabinet, monitor, and circuit board, and smaller ones that were sold as boards only. In the early 1990s, Namco's strength lay in large game machines incorporating 3-D computer graphics technology. It struggled in the smaller game machine market, where it competed with superior combat games such as Capcom's Street Fighter. Longing to become better known in this market, Namco was looking for an opportunity to take the market by storm with its biggest technology weapon: 3-D computer graphics.

Then Virtua Fighter was released and Namco witnessed 3-D computer graphics succeeding in a large business model. A proposal was made by SCEI at Namco for development of a combat game based on System 22, but the company was hesitant: "Using System 22, which was developed for large arcade game machines, is just following Sega's example. We have no experience of combat games using 3-D computer graphics. By the time we've finished developing our game machine, Sega will be launching a new, improved version of Virtua Fighter." Others at Namco thought that direct competition within the company would be counterproductive.

PS/X made its appearance just as Namco was struggling with this dilemma. Senior Managing Director Nakamura thought that the PlayStation technology would work for Namco. Tekken, an arcade game developed using PlayStation technology, was released on December 15, 1994, shortly after the PlayStation's debut.

A SHOT ACROSS THE BOW AT COMPETITORS

There was another reason for Namco's decision to participate in the PlayStation project. "The timing of Sony's proposal was just perfect for us, because we were beginning to feel the limitations of being a Nintendo third-party supplier," Nakamura confesses. When Sony began seeking Namco's help, Namco happened to be looking for a new platform; as if by karmic attraction, each company was seeking the other.

There had been a time when Namco seriously considered moving into the market for home-use game hardware, but the company had abandoned the idea because the business plan was not feasible. Estimates for the LSI circuit alone were $100 or more. To make a profit on software, even if it meant losing money on hardware, the machine had to be priced at $150 or less, and the company would have to sell 3 million units in the first eighteen months or the platform would be considered a failure. This meant eighteen months' inventory—3 million units, or $400,000,000 in capital—had to be prepared. This was simply not possible for Namco.

Nakamura explains: "We wanted to produce home-use 3-D game machines utilizing the know-how we had acquired from arcade games, but we couldn't do it with the Super Famicom, and we had no hardware of our own. The only solution was to use a platform that could handle 3-D computer graphics."

A year after the release of the Famicom, Namco had entered the market with hit software titles such as Pacman and Zebius. Initially, Namco enjoyed special treatment among the Famicom third-party suppliers; it was granted "most favored" status by Nintendo, which meant that it got certain privileges, such as higher royalties than those received by other software houses.

Five years later, however, following the release of the Super Famicom, Namco was suddenly demoted to a status about equal to that of other software developers. Forced to compete on equal terms with other software makers, Namco's margins were whittled down. Namco longed to have its own hardware to open up new business frontiers, but this simply wasn't a realistic goal. Around this time, a man asked to meet with Namco executives. The man was Kutaragi.

"I asked Mr. Kutaragi about the dispute between Sony and Nintendo, which we'd heard about, and Sony said that they wanted to make their own home-use game hardware," Nakamura recalls. "But that's what we wanted to do, too, and when I mentioned that, he became wary."

Soon afterward, the newspaper *Nippon Kogyo Shinbun* published a scoop on its front page about Sony's development of an innovative image-processing integrated circuit (IC). Nakamura realized that this might be the graphics engine built into the PlayStation. He telephoned Kutaragi to ask, but Kutaragi pretended to know nothing about it. Nakamura persisted, and finally Kutaragi told him about the PS/X project.

In the fall of 1993, Namco released the arcade game Ridge Racer, a testament to the company's improved 3-D capabilities. Around this time, 3-D technology was becoming much more refined, and Namco began to wonder whether Ridge Racer could be developed for use in the home. Sony's demonstration at its No. 10 Auditorium heightened the enthusiasm within Namco to create a home-use version of Ridge Racer.

"Sony showed us 3-D computer graphics on one of their prototypes," says Senior Managing Director Nakamura. "Personally, I wasn't that surprised, because it was something that I had predicted would happen. The photograph taken of our President Nakamura and Sony's President Ohga shaking hands is what I remember of the occasion."

Since Namco and Sega were archrivals in the arcade-game market, Namco couldn't supply software for the Sega Saturn and had to back the PlayStation instead. Boosting sales of the PlayStation in the head-to-head competition with the Saturn became one of Namco's top priorities. "Since Namco was participating in the PlayStation project, we very much wanted it to become the leader among platforms," says Namco director Haraguchi. "We even stopped all development of software for the Super Famicom to commit ourselves a hundred percent to the PlayStation. This was a huge commitment, because to that point we had sold more than ten billion yen in Super Famicom software. We can't change formats on a whim."

The race car game genre was one of the first to take advantage of hardware innovation. Namco's Ridge Racer, the first PlayStation game to hit the market, proved to be an enormous hit. Users were astounded that they could now enjoy at home a game that had previously been available only in arcades. Says Nakamura, "At one stage, unit sales of Ridge Racer outstripped PlayStation console sales."

For game enthusiasts, going from a two-dimensional to a three-dimensional screen was a great leap forward. Ridge Racer could generate three-dimensional images of vehicles, and it could even produce 3-D images that gave the game player the impression of driving backward on the course.

Says Maruyama (today vice chairman of SCEI), "Namco is really important to us. Looking back, the video-game market was like an Othello game. In Othello, however well you may be doing you will lose everything at the end unless you capture the corners. With the PlayStation project we began capturing corners when Namco decided to sign on." Sony took one corner with Namco, another with the software developer Square two years later, and a third with Enix Corporation, a software developer.

The competition between the PlayStation and the Sega Saturn was fierce in December 1996, but with the release of Final Fantasy in January 1997 the Playstation began to increase its lead over the Saturn. Maruyama says he cannot thank Namco enough for creating this opportunity.

HARDWARE TO ATTRACT SOFTWARE DEVELOPERS:
3-D COMPUTER GRAPHICS

Sony's principal tactic in attracting software developers was a strategic unveiling of 3-D technology. At first, Sony would explain the technology verbally, which usually failed to elicit much interest from representatives of the software houses. Then, perhaps during a second meeting, Sony representatives would deliver the knockout punch—a video demonstrating 3-D computer graphics PlayStation-style. Seeing truly was believing in the case of promoting the PlayStation: In most cases, the video won over the executives and put the software house in the PlayStation stable.

Sony first visited Company D on May 28, 1993. Their response was cool and they put the ball back into Sony's court: "We're not interested unless you can sell one million units in the first year. And it's no use unless Sony makes its own, high-quality software. The price must be below ¥20,000. We don't have much faith in consumer electronics companies, because they're so slow to make decisions."

During the second meeting, when Company D was shown the demonstration video, the response was totally different: "It's so stunning, we can't believe you can make it for under 50,000 yen. People involved with computer graphics [Company D was using workstations to make 3-D computer graphics images for TV commercials for its own products] will wonder why game machines have become more advanced than PCs. We didn't think a 3-D computer graphics game machine was possible, but we're truly impressed. The texture rendering and the moving computer graphics dinosaur are wonderful. An average game maker won't be able to create software for it." The "seeing is believing" effect was overwhelming.

During the May 28 initial meeting, Company E said evasively: "We aren't sure how serious Sony is about this business.

However brilliant the hardware may be, it won't sell if it's expensive. And however wonderful the technology, it won't sell well unless it's what users want. In principle we would consider participating, but we can't commit ourselves until we know more about the specifications."

After seeing the demonstration video at the second meeting, on July 21, Company E changed its attitude completely: "The performance is phenomenal. It's much better than we expected. Technically it's terrific, but we can't make the final decision to participate until we know when Sony will finalize its worldwide marketing strategy."

At Konami's first meeting with Sony on June 24, Managing Director Kitagami's response was lukewarm: "You haven't made clear in your proposal anything that explains the choice of CD-ROM as a medium, and how that makes new games possible. If the performance is similar to Megadrive and PC Engine performance, then we would prefer to wait until the price of mask ROM [the medium used in Nintendo's Super Famicom] falls. You say the image quality of games has improved, but there's a limit to what can be achieved on home-use TVs."

Sony showed Kitagami a demonstration video at its Aoyama office on August 23, and Kutaragi gave him the specifications verbally. Kitagami's response was "I can't believe it. If the image is really moving, it's a tremendous breakthrough. This type of real-time action isn't even possible with arcade games. How can it be done on a home-use machine? Are you using a special kind of device? Can you really make a home-use machine out of this?"

Before the PlayStation, graphics expression in home-use game machines involved a technique called sprite, whereby 2-D images such as characters were moved by scrolling the background. The PS/X images shown on the demo tape showed more than one 3-D computer-generated character moving simultaneously, with the screen giving an impression of depth. To produce this effect, the machine needs the capability to renew the image in real time in one-sixtieth of a second (the time it takes to compose one TV field), as well as a follow-up mechanism that responds instantaneously to controller input, synthesizes, and displays images. For this the hardware must conduct a tremendous number of image-information-processing calculations. At the time it was considered virtually impossible to do all the real-time calculating operations with a single CPU, even with high-performance, business-use graphics workstations, which all used plenty of specialist hardware in addition to CPUs and dedicated 3-D processors called DSPs. This is why Kitagami was astonished by the PlayStation.

"You can't produce images like this without a formidable custom IC base," Kitagami said. "Sony is obviously putting a lot of effort into this. The hardware is so incredible, I can't say right now what software ideas we'll come up with. I think we'll find out as we get accustomed to using it. If you can sell the hardware for less than 30,000 yen, you'll probably be able to dominate the games market."

Kitagami's comment about the "formidable IC base" was correct. "This image couldn't be produced by combining general-purpose devices," Kutaragi explains. "In those days, the basic performance of Mips Technologies' R3000 general-purpose RISC chip was 30 MIPS [MIPS is a unit of measure denoting execution of one million instructions per second]. Even if you used ten of these, you'd only get 300 MIPS. For natural-looking 3-D computer graphics based on texture mapping [the technique used to make 3-D computer graphics appear realistic], 2-D sprite drawing of the same standard as arcade games, and real-time decoding of moving images, we needed the DSP equivalent of 800 MIPS." With his years of experience in the field,

Kitagami immediately understood the sheer superiority of the PlayStation's technology.

HARDWARE DESIGN—CD-ROM: DESTROYING PRECONCEIVED NOTIONS

Another strategy that was effective in attracting software makers was the choice of CD-ROM, an optical disk medium, instead of the mask ROM used in the Super Famicom. PlayStation was the first platform to clearly reveal the latent potential of CD-ROM. This had a tremendous and far-reaching effect on technology, marketing, and even distribution, a subject that will be addressed in the next chapter. Suffice it to say here that Sony's choice of CD-ROM resulted in debates with a software developer that became an incentive for the software house to participate in the PlayStation project.

The software house asked Sony, "We hear you've chosen CD-ROM as the medium, but doesn't that mean slow access time?" The question made sense. CD-ROM games were already in existence for Sega's Megadrive and NEC's PC Engine, but they had extremely slow access speeds and were difficult to operate, and conventional wisdom had it that CD-ROM was unsuitable for video games.

Kutaragi, however, loved this kind of question, because one of the most powerful ways to accentuate the PlayStation's capabilities was to explain the way CD-ROM was employed. He explains: "Certainly slow access time is a structural problem with CD-ROM, but this criticism does not apply to the PS/X. For example, Matsushita's 3-DO is a data-replay type machine, so access time directly affects software performance. Even with a two-speed drive, you can only get a data transmission speed of twice 150 kilobytes or 300 kilobytes per second, which makes the game speed very slow. The PlayStation is an image-generation system, not a data-replay system. Once the data has been read from the CD, the image-generation engine works at full speed, quickly generating and synthesizing images one after another. This is where it's totally different from other game machines."

The concept of using CD-ROM in an entirely new approach was revolutionary at a time when "CD-ROM is slow" was the conventional wisdom. PS/X also offered interesting functions to creators. While it is only natural with a real-time computer graphics method that creates images in the machine itself, the PlayStation required much smaller volumes of data than other CD-ROM formats like PC Engine (signal volumes can be compared by checking the signal surface area of the CD).

The data volume of Ridge Racer, Namco's first PlayStation game, is two megabytes. The total capacity of a CD-ROM is 650 megabytes, so Ridge Racer uses just 0.3 percent of total volume. What did this mean to Namco's creators? Once the PlayStation has read the Ridge Racer program from the CD-ROM, it has is no further use for the CD. Because there was so much excess storage capacity, the creators filled it up with music data. They even added a minigame that ran while Ridge Racer was loading so users did not notice how long the process took. The ability to enjoy the game while playing music became an unexpected selling point of Ridge Racer. The PlayStation's unique feature of providing a large-capacity CD for a small-volume game proved to be popular among software creators.

Later on, game fanatics discovered that once the data were loaded they could continue playing the game after replacing the game CD with a music CD. Some users then began to enjoy the Ridge Racer driving experience while playing *enka* (traditional Japanese popular music). Other new combinations of music and game-playing developed, such as playing *shogi* to reggae. At one point, this feature became a hot topic on NiftyServe, an Internet connector service, forums. Kutaragi had foreseen all this when he proposed a combination of computer graphics and CD-ROM. And this was not the only feature he prepared to grab the attention of software creators and users alike.

SOFTWARE DESIGN TO ATTRACT SOFTWARE DEVELOPERS

Having brought software makers into the fold, the next step was to have them produce as many software titles as possible. One of Sony Music's basic business philosophies was described in the following exchange during an interview:

"Who do you think is the most important person in a record company, Mr. Asakura?"

"Top management? Someone like you, Mr. Maruyama?"

"The most important person in a record company is neither the producer nor the director, not even the president. It's the musician. We have to believe that the musician is God. You must maintain this attitude even with a new artist. Not all up-and-coming artists are going to sell, but you must treat even ones that don't sell with the same attitude."

According to Maruyama, if a music company doesn't treat new artists with respect, they may retaliate in the future. If a young artist whom you treated with indifference and removed from your list is later successful, the relationship will remain sour, but if you had looked after him or her as an artist, there might be opportunities in the future. He concludes: "So it's important to be humble when dealing with new artists. This is an essential rule for a company dealing in intellectual property."

An outstanding aspect of the PlayStation concept is that this artist-management theory was transplanted unchanged into the world of computer games. Music and games are the same in that the creator/artist produces the software or game; therefore, Sony must treat game creators well. This means providing an environment that facilitates game development and makes creators feel positive about their work.

Learning from Maruyama's artist-management theory, Kutaragi devised a program that would help game creators. Time was short; specifications were disclosed to software companies in early 1994, with less than a year to go before the PlayStation went on sale. How could software development time be minimized? The answer was to motivate software creators, to make them eager to create games for the PlayStation. Toward this end, providing a creator-friendly environment at the earliest possible stage was essential.

Kutaragi demonstrated his unusual talent at this point by insisting that all hardware functions that support creators be produced and refined in-house instead of outsourcing the PlayStation's LSI circuit layout and manufacture. He explains: "Sony makes the set itself and several semiconductor manufacturers make the LSI circuits, but we wanted to concentrate our development power on improving software development tools. We provide an environment for communicating with games programmers via a dedicated network, giving them as much support as possible on a long-term basis. We can offer this service because we understand the technical details of the PlayStation. This joint effort gives creators more time to produce what they want. So we began working on dedicated PlayStation library software alongside hardware development; if anything, we worked harder on the library."

A library is the common software needed for game production. "I adopted the same principle as used in Chinese cooking," Kutaragi explains. "Although there are a great many dishes in Chinese cuisine, each dish is served within a short time of ordering. Chinese dishes have a short cooking time, because each dish isn't made by a single chef from beginning to end; a division-of-labor system is used, with different people doing the shopping and preparation before the actual cooking stage."

Shinichi Okamoto, today software development manager at SCEI's Software Division, who developed the library under Kutaragi's direction, likens the system to an automotive plant: "When you make an automobile, you use screws in many different places. You use the same screws for different models. It's the same principle."

In other words, rather than application-specific software, the library contains software that is required no matter the game being created. For example, the library includes the software used to read data from the CD-ROM or memory card. In other words, it is software that does not have the characteristics of a particular title.

THE LIBRARY, ALTHOUGH THE TARGET OF MUCH OPPOSITION, WAS A NECESSARY EVIL

Without a library game, creators must analyze the hardware and produce even shared-application software from scratch. The library solves the problem and allows game developers to devote more time to creative thinking. This development style was virtually nonexistent before the PlayStation, so Kutaragi's team expected creators to find it both innovative and helpful. The reality was not as they had imagined, as Okamoto, who was involved in dealing with this aspect, discovered.

Okamoto was the fifth software engineer to join SCEI. None of the four engineers who joined before him had ever dealt with game software as products. After pondering what they might do, they decided to narrow their target. "We focused on software used by videogame software creators," says Okamoto. "Our perspective was how to make creators enjoy producing games for us. If we provided such software, we thought, more software houses would join the PlayStation camp."

What kind of software did he mean? In fact, he had no idea. This should come as no surprise, because none of the software development team had had any experience with games. Nonetheless, they couldn't waste their time lamenting their own lack of expertise and they began basic library design in December 1992. "All we had was faith and conviction that a particular software program was essential in a common library. Instead of making things customers asked us to make, we made whatever we believed they would need."

They did not write software that could be used only for specific titles, because the point of a library is that it can be used by all. Although on some occasions they provided a customized library as a "component" of a specific title, this would always be added to the main library the next time around. Not only would benefiting a particular software house be contrary to the law of fairness, but Sony wanted every useful addition to the main library to make it more advanced. Okamoto explains: "Take software that speeds up combat games, for example. First of all, we made customized software for a particular maker that asked for 'accelerator type' software to increase the speed of characters' actions. After it was completed and we confirmed that using the software made the movements faster, we added it to the public library. Then everyone was able to benefit."

If the library was that good, surely all creators welcomed its appearance? The reality was not so straightforward. After SCEI started supplying the library, the company encountered problems with persuading creators to use it. When asked why, a creator replied: "I don't like using a program written by someone else as is." His argument was that if he encountered problems caused by the library, he couldn't deal with them because he didn't know what was in the library. Therefore, he didn't want to use the library if he could possibly help it. Software creators mostly agreed that they preferred to write the whole program, even though it meant additional work, because they could identify the cause of problems in programs they had written themselves.

This way of thinking was typical of game creators, most of whom like to control the whole content of the software themselves. They dislike the ambiguity of a situation in which they cannot be certain whether the cause of a problem lay in the library on in their own work.

"Until I heard this, I didn't realize creators thought this way," Okamoto confesses. Creators often demanded to know whether Sony would improve the content of the library or whether it could make changes to the software. Okamoto would reply, "No, we can't do that. It's common software available to everyone, so we can't modify it for a particular application." The creators would still persist, however, saying, "But isn't it because of the Sony library that the movements are so slow?" Creators suspected that the library software was responsible for slowing down their title's image movement.

Okamoto would then reply, "Please rest assured that our library has no effect on the visible parts of your game," but creators rarely believed him. He described a typical occurrence at conferences attended by overseas software houses as follows: "First, I would explain how the PlayStation software works. Then someone would raise his hand and say, 'Please disclose the library source code.' Then the whole audience of two hundred or so would applaud. A standing ovation from everyone! The same thing happened everywhere we went. I couldn't believe it."

Creators' dissatisfaction lay in the fact that, in spite of the understandable existence of an unwritten rule that game machines must not change formats for several years, the specifications of the semiconductors used in platforms progressed considerably over that period. This means that, although the software appears to be the same, progressive changes are made to the hardware at the core of the platform. For this reason, machine makers cannot easily disclose the specifications of the hardware itself, because then they couldn't guarantee compatibility.

With existing game machines it was possible to give direct instructions to the circuitry. Hardware specifications of the Famicom were in the public domain, and direct instructions could be given to the hardware. This was possible because the system itself was relatively simple, but with something as complex as the PlayStation it was difficult to ensure the compatibility of application software when changes were made to the hardware. A part of the operating system called the "kernel" and a group of basic programs such as device drivers are responsible for ensuring compatibility. Game programmers become frustrated, however, because they are unable to make changes directly to these programs.

Says Senior Managing Director Nakamura of Namco, "That's why at the beginning the fact that we couldn't operate the machine ourselves was a source of stress. It's like scratching an itch on your foot without being able to take your shoe off; it's really frustrating. The team developing arcade games were especially frustrated because with all previous arcade games they could work directly on the hardware. Sony would say, 'Games creators like you shouldn't have to worry about such details,' but it was confusing for us, because we'd never worked in this way before."

In spite of all the negative reactions, Okamoto persisted in communicating the benefits of the library. He argued that the use of common resources was crucial in making game software, as illustrated by the dramatic increase in application software after PC operating systems progressed from DOS to Windows.

His appeal slowly began to have some effect. Gradually, game developers began to comment that when they used the library, the number of development processes decreased and the work was surprisingly easy. Indeed, it was thanks to the library that Namco was able to transplant Ridge Racer from arcade game to PlayStation with a development time of under a year, and Takara succeeded in developing Battle Arena Toshinden in a short period of time. Some developers began to say that they would rely on the library for part of the development because it made such an improvement in efficiency. And enhancing library content would also reduce creators' workload.

Initially, the library covered only the C programming language and 3-D technology. A 2-D technology library was added in response to creator requests, with their feedback reflected in the content. The library has been upgraded several times since then. "For example, someone pointed out that there was something wrong with an argument in a function in the C library, so we checked it out, and found that they were right. So we immediately rectified it," says Okamoto. The problem was not so simple, however. The library consists of basic software used by all creators, and although some might think a particular operation isn't quite right, it might work perfectly well for others. The reason for this is differences in environment—PC and tool software.

Okamoto explains: "We would fix something because someone asked us to, only to find that someone else objected, demanding to know why we were changing it. This happened so frequently that we decided halfway through the process of building the library to retain the original software and put version numbers on revised versions. So the original would be number one, the first one to be revised would be version two, then version three, and so on. Some even went up to version nine. It is a bit embarrassing for our library staff to have so many versions, because it means the original wasn't very good!"

In this way the library grew. Initially there were only about 350 functions, but today there are 1,800. At one stage, eighteen employees were involved in library development. "Of course, they had plenty of support from us," Namco Senior Managing Director Nakamura comments. "Today the end result is pretty impressive, but when we began developing Ridge Racer in May 1993, the library had only the bare minimum of necessary functions. We were the ones that really built up the library. We cooperated with the library development staff by telling them what items and functions we wanted. From Sony's point of view, we are more of a second-party than a third-party developer."

The results of Sony's dedication to creating an environment conducive to software creation are plain for all to see. Through this process the library developers enabled third-party developers to produce many software products, supporting the PlayStation's dramatic growth from behind the scenes. "But our role is definitely backstage," Okamoto laments. "Support work means being an unsung hero. It's unglamorous work, and students don't like to do it. SCEI has recently become a popular employer with new graduates, but they all want to make games and won't even consider doing support. It's so disappointing. I'd like for more people to understand the importance of support work."

4

CHAPTER

Distribution Revolution: The "Breakout" Strategy

"What we wanted to do with the PlayStation," reveals Vice President Akira Sato of SCEI, "was to promote a concept that was clearly differentiated from anyone else's. In other words, we wanted to compete in a different arena altogether." Sony believed that, being late to market with the PlayStation, it should stake out a new battleground instead of copying its predecessors and so cause distributors, software houses, and subsequently end users to switch to Sony's approach. The primary secret to Sony's victory with the PlayStation lay in its technological superiority, which clearly impressed third-party suppliers. But that alone could not have produced such outstanding success. This is obvious from Sato's words: "When we thought about entering this business, we wondered how we could retain our own identity. Because we had no previous experience in the market, we resolved to impress users by creating something that would make them think, 'Wow, Sony is a cut above its competitors!'"

It was this attitude that carried the day. If Sony had followed a traditional business model in the game market, it could not have dreamed of such remarkable success. Sato proclaims: "As intruders, we could operate freely without being restricted by industry conventions. From the industry's perspective, competition arose from an unexpected source."

MASK ROM DISRUPTS THE DISTRIBUTION CHANNEL

Why did Sato feel that he had to start a distribution revolution? His resolve was partly based on bitter personal experience. Some time previously he had bought Super Famicom software from a store near his home. He couldn't find on display the popular title he sought, so he told the owner of the store what he was looking for. The owner went off to the back of the store and shortly returned with the title, treating it like something precious and saying, "This is what you want, isn't it?"

Sato took the software home and connected the Famicom to the TV, only to find that there was something wrong; to his disgust, points scored by a previous player were displayed on the screen. Although it looked brand new, the software was unmistakably used. And he had paid the full price! He rushed back to the store to complain, and the storekeeper apologized meekly: "I'm sorry. You're right. It's definitely a used product."

Such practices were commonplace in the game market before the arrival of the PlayStation. Says Sato: "Dissatisfaction will mount if users are treated that way; they were clearly being cheated. There's no doubt that people in the game business don't respect users. This experience made me determined to change the trading practices in the computer game market."

At that time Sato was merely another Super Famicom user, but complaints about the method of distribution were increasing sharply among software makers as well. Says Managing Director Kitagami of Konami: "We were losing our patience with the Shoshinkai, the Nintendo wholesaler organization. They wouldn't replace faulty products, they traded without regard for proper channels, they even copied software. They behaved so unethically, it was beyond belief. How could they get away with it?"

The game industry's distribution structure was complex and mysterious to outsiders. The conventional channel was from Shoshinkai wholesaler to retail store, but secondary wholesalers and cash wholesalers often operated between the two. Practices such as retailers returning products purchased from wholesalers and wholesalers diverting the products to a different store were commonplace. Selling a used product as a new one, a practice that Sato experienced, was only the tip of the iceberg. One example of a more insidious practice is "dummy rental." A retailer sells a new software product for $50, which is below the store's cost. Users will be attracted to the deal because the price is so low. The retailer then buys back the software from the same customers at an even lower price and sells it again for $50. Let's assume that the profit on the sale is $10. By repeating the buying and selling process ten times, the retailer earns a profit of $100. The more times the retailer turns over the same product, the greater the profit.

THE LIMITATIONS OF A MEDIUM UNSUITED TO REPEAT PRODUCTION

Famicom software was distributed in a unique way. A Shoshinkai wholesaler would conclude a contract with a software company for bulk purchase of a title. The purchase would be for large quantities—say, 5,000 or 10,000 units. This is fine if the title is a hit, but otherwise the wholesaler will end up with a large inventory of unsold stock. And in reality, only a few titles are popular enough to sell in such high quantities.

Sellers exhibit a certain type of behavior under this kind of distribution structure. Wholesalers fear inventory buildup and make an effort to off-load the software they have purchased as quickly as possible. If the software is a sure seller, however, they are reluctant to sell and hang on to it for as long as possible, waiting for prices to rise.

Where the Famicom was concerned, the cause of this behavior lay in the characteristics of mask ROM (semiconductor memory packaged in an oblong cartridge) as a medium. The advantage of mask ROM is its quick data access, a feature much appreciated by users. From the manufacturer's point of view, however, mask ROM has the critical flaw of being time-consuming to produce. Manufacturers place additional orders in a panic if a hit product sells out, but mask ROM is a semiconductor product with a long manufacturing lead time— more than two months. Timing is crucial in the game business; sales opportunities will not wait. Software houses frequently suffered the experience of ending up with unsold inventory of a product because it took two months to replenish the stock, by which time its popularity had waned.

This was an inevitable problem for a medium whose physical characteristics were so removed from their content requirements. Mask ROM takes a long time to manufacture, so in practice repeat production is impossible. Fearing the loss of sales opportunities, game manufacturers will produce large quantities of the same title. Wholesalers, however, cannot hold all the stock and so dispose of part of their inventory by selling it to other wholesalers or cash wholesalers. This led to the many problems described above. The situation was truly a vicious circle.

"Although I was tricked into buying a used item," says Sato, "that business model is the right one for mask ROM. Since repeat production is impossible, a receptacle must be provided somewhere in the distribution system. If mask ROM had been adopted for the PlayStation, we would have used a distribution strategy similar to Nintendo's. There's no other option."

Temporary demand for mask ROM products arises easily. A retail store wants to buy a large supply of a title that is selling well, but because no single wholesaler can obtain a sufficient quantity, the store contacts other wholesalers. Several wholesalers receive an identical order and the total demand appears to be enormous. A large portion of this, however, is fictitious demand.

Only a few companies carried out precise market research and measured and understood software sales trends. Namco was one of them. Says Senior Managing Director Nakamura: "To ensure that mask ROM products would be on store shelves on the release date, we had to deliver the master copy to Nintendo three months in advance. Taking end-of-year demand into account, production had to start in August. But how can you predict end-of-year demand accurately in August? If you forecast sales of 300,000 units and actual demand was for 400,000, you've lost the opportunity to sell 100,000 copies. Or in the opposite case, you end up with surplus stock of 100,000. When we made Nintendo games, we had to sneak out late at night to dispose of excess inventory on several occasions. You have to be a genius to predict mask ROM production and sales."

To avoid missing business opportunities, Namco tried to find ways to turn market trends to its advantage, even with mask ROM products. The company even attempted to explore the possibility of repeat orders. Sato was surprised when he heard this story: Namco was the rare exception. In the game industry, it was customary for manufacturers to build in a "risk insurance" component (usually $5) when calculating cost. With mask ROM the inventory risk was so great that nervous managers at software houses required compensating security.

CD-ROM: THE ONLY SOLUTION

The use of mask ROM brought serious problems to retail stores, users, and the management ranks of game manufacturers. The major disadvantage of mask ROM for retailers and software developers was the impossibility of making accurate sales forecasts. It was an exceedingly high-risk, high-return business for game manufacturers, because the developer would suffer shortages if a product sold well, but would end up with huge inventories if sales were disappointing. A decision on production volume could not be made without forecasting market trends three months ahead, which in reality is an impossible task. Therefore, decision making was extremely difficult. Retail stores wanted to know the maximum sales potential for a product, but demand for hit products outpaced supply, whereas poor sellers resulted in excess inventory.

There were problems for users, as well. First of all, the software was expensive. This is primarily due to the high manufacturing cost of mask ROM. Software houses had to pay Nintendo an OEM manufacturing fee of $30 per copy, and after development cost, margin, risk insurance, and distribution costs were factored in, the final retail price approached $100.

The second problem was Nintendo's pricing strategy. Says Kutaragi, who worked with Nintendo for a long time: "Nintendo's idea was to increase software prices over time. Instead of releasing software at an affordable price, it would restrict software to a small, high-quality selection and push up the price every time the format moved into a new generation. Back then, they believed in driving up software prices."

Software prices for the 8-bit Famicom were around $40, and almost $100 for the Super Famicom, as a result of Nintendo's insistence on keeping software prices high. "It's ridiculous from an end user's point of view," Kutaragi comments. "It's very annoying for parents when software prices go up every year in late December and early January, and for kids too, because they can afford to buy only a limited number of titles with their limited spending money. Kids then begin to demonstrate a form of self-defense by playing the game as quickly as possible and taking it to a used-software outlet while it still has a high resale value. Soon it became commonplace for elementary school pupils to trade used software for thousands of yen, so they introduced a rule that youngsters had to bring a consent form signed by their parents before they could sell software. I knew that such a crazy situation could not last indefinitely."

Against the backdrop of the game industry's retail and distribution system, which bordered on the anarchic, Sony began to see the correct distribution strategy for PlayStation. If

Sony was to bring a new product onto the market, its software had to be something that satisfied all three market participants: software producers, retailers, and end users. Moreover, it had to allow management to formulate less risky selling strategies, enable retailers to make accurate sales forecasts, and be priced so that users could afford to buy it, even children spending their pocket money.

There was only one solution: to use CD-ROM as the medium. Kutaragi had first considered using CD-ROM when he was struggling to persuade Nintendo to adopt Sony's technology. Nintendo was experiencing a sense of crisis amid rumors that Sega was working on a 16-bit system and NEC planned to enter the market. Sony and Nintendo agreed to organize a summer business camp to discuss the next-generation Famicom at a Sony resort in Mikkabi, Shizuoka Prefecture, halfway between Tokyo and Kyoto. Lively debate ensued over three days and two nights starting on June 16, 1987.

Even at this early stage, Kutaragi proposed to Nintendo that they should use CD-ROM instead of mask ROM. It is clear that Kutaragi had favored the CD-ROM as a medium for many years. However, Nintendo's view was that mask ROM capacity would increase in the future, and they did not make any immediate decision. In 1989, when development of Nintendo's Super Famicom had reached the final stage, Kutaragi suggested again to Nintendo that it use CD-ROM. Nintendo, however, remained negative about CD-ROM, mindful of the poor sales performance of the Famicom disk adapter, and eventually asked Sony to work on it alone. Sony, therefore, began to develop in earnest a CD-ROM system compatible with the Super Famicom. The following year, the presidents of Sony and Nintendo signed a joint development agreement for the CD-ROM system. On June 2, 1991, Nintendo and Philips announced at the CES that they were to develop a CD-ROM system that would not be compatible with Sony's.

REVOLUTIONIZING THE DISTRIBUTION SYSTEM

Why did Kutaragi back CD-ROM? First, it was far cheaper and had greater storage capacity than mask ROM. It also offered multimedia benefits, since it combined image, sound, and digital data. Moreover, it was highly strategic as a software supply medium. Kutaragi's team not only focused on the medium's basic characteristics, such as low price and large capacity, but also analyzed CD-ROM from various perspectives and took full advantage of its rich strategic attributes. Clearly, their goal was to revolutionize the distribution system with CD-ROM.

CD-ROM had been used since 1990 as a game medium—Sega's Mega CD and NEC's PC Engine are prime examples—but no company had ever adopted CD-ROM as a medium with the intention of reforming the distribution system. CD-ROM was sold only in a limited market, distributed through the existing mask ROM product channels.

With the PlayStation, however, Sony made a deliberate attempt to emphasize the advantages of CD-ROM and use it to ignite a distribution revolution. First, Kutaragi's team stressed the attractive price of CD-ROM. They believed that the lower software prices made possible by using CD-ROM were a benefit that would not only satisfy users' needs, but would become the driving force behind distribution reform. Sony knew that the lower prices would be a powerful weapon to compete against the established format.

One indication of this was the used-software market, which in those days was essential to end users. Top-selling software would sell out immediately, with the less popular titles remaining on retailers' shelves. Thus, the only way people could obtain popular titles was through used-software dealers who bought these titles on the secondhand market.

Just when Kutaragi had decided that there was something very wrong with the situation, Sato had an inspiration. "This is the biggest weakness of the mask ROM business model," he said. "We can defeat the established manufacturers if we create a situation in which consumers can buy hit titles new, and whenever they want, at a price lower than that of used cartridges."

His thinking went like this: Super Famicom software retailing for $100 is sold to a used-software dealer for $50. The dealer adds a $20 margin and resells it for $70. If new PlayStation games could retail for less than $70, it should be possible for Sony to defeat its competitors. Furthermore, if the titles that had been circulating in the used-software market could be replaced by new ones, the profit from the secondhand market could be redirected to sales of new products.

The Sony team had discovered an inviting market opportunity by calmly analyzing the market's status quo. Kutaragi explains: "That's why we set the retail price of most PlayStation software at $58. The way to solve the problems with the old order was to offer new software at low prices. This was a deliberate, strategic move. The price was about half that of a mask ROM cartridge and in the same range as the early Famicom software."

Before the release of the PlayStation, mask ROM software prices were on the increase. Twenty-four of the Super Famicom titles released between October 1993 and September 1994 were priced above $100, more than double the number of the previous year. "With mask ROM, the developer builds the profit to be made in the used-software market into the retail price, so the price of new products is high," says Sato. "We used CD-ROM to change this absurd situation."

THE MEANS TO APPEAL TO SOFTWARE HOUSES

The appeal of CD-ROM for software producers would be reduced in proportion to the decrease in profits. Thus, it was essential to develop a business model that enabled software producers to make a reasonable profit even if the retail price of the software was slashed by 50 percent.

One way of looking at the PlayStation is as a series of cleverly contrived attractions. The attraction for software creators were 3-D computer graphics and the library, whereas the attraction for management was the business advantages of using CD-ROM as the software supply medium. First, CD-ROM has a far lower manufacturing cost than mask ROM—a cost advantage that Sony could use as an enticement to executives of software houses who were thinking of participating in the PlayStation platform: "We can make the software inexpensive. *And* you'll make a good profit."

Low cost means a low investment. Consider the following example: In the case of mask ROM, the OEM price is $30 per copy: $300,000 for 10,000 units, $1,800,000 for 60,000 units. There is a time lag between the actual sale and when the software producer receives the proceeds, so the company must have enough working capital to operate during this period. In the case of the PlayStation, however, the manufacturing cost of a CD-ROM is $9 per copy, or $540,000 for 60,000 units. This cost advantage would be appreciated by software makers who had creative ability but lacked capital.

Once the initial outlay has been calculated, the next step is to work out the profit. The retail price of a Super Famicom title is $100, compared with $58 for a PlayStation title. Sony guaranteed that its distribution system would maintain and even increase gross margins for software houses in spite of the software's lower prices. And the general framework of the distribution system would remain in line with industry conventions. This was the clever aspect of the PlayStation project: Although Sony the innovator had surpassed the existing technology, media, and marketing models, it would remain faithful to Nintendo's practices with respect to manufacturing structure and royalty concept.

Nintendo's royalty system worked as follows: The platform developer produced all the software under an OEM agreement (that is, under the software producer's brand name), and the software house paid the platform maker an OEM production fee and royalties. Says Sato, "We used Nintendo's basic royalty business formula unchanged. It was a perfectly good system, so there was no need for us to change it. Royalties are like a tax you pay on developing for the format."

Although the overall structure of Sony's arrangement with software developers was the same as Nintendo's, the details were far more favorable to software producers, whose main gripe had been the high royalties and OEM production fees. Sony realized that this weakness in Nintendo's system should be exploited. The physical manufacturing cost of CD-ROM is a tenth that of mask ROM. Sony thought that a new OEM production fee and royalty schedule that took maximum advantage of the low manufacturing cost would be attractive to software houses, many of whom had told Sony that smaller profits for them would not be acceptable.

The following is a profit-and-loss calculation model that assumes mask ROM sales of 100,000 units and software development cost of $1 million. The Super Famicom platform's OEM price is $30 per unit, which includes the mask ROM cost of $15 per unit. In other words, the software houses pay Nintendo a royalty of $15 per unit for manufacturing the title.

The software houses include development cost and equipment amortization of $10 per unit. To this they add a profit of $10 per unit, an advertising cost of $6 per unit, and the $5 risk insurance (security against the risks associated with mask ROM, which is not suited to repeat production). The above factors total $61, which is the price to the wholesaler. The wholesaler's profit is $12 and the retailer's profit is $25, which brings the final retail price to $98.

By contrast, PlayStation software is suited to repeat production, so the $5 risk insurance does not apply. Software houses pay Sony a $9 OEM production fee, which includes the royalty and CD-ROM manufacturing cost. Add to this $10 in software development and equipment-amortization cost, the software producers' profit of $10, and advertising cost of $6; the total of $35 is the price to wholesalers. This is $26 less than the price of Super Famicom software.

The wholesaler (in the case of SCEI) takes a profit of $6 and the retailer's margin is $17, bringing the final total to $58. Thus, although the retail price was lower than for Super Famicom software, software house profit was the same $10, which meant there was no reason for them to object. This royalty system provided a strong incentive when Sony was inviting software producers to join the PlayStation camp. Most software houses agreed with Namco director Haraguchi, who says: "We thought the OEM price was reasonable. The $9 OEM fee [this has now been changed to a percentage rate] covered SCEI's hardware development costs, support, and format promotion costs, so it was a fair figure."

USING CD-ROM TO FREE DEVELOPERS FROM LOCKING IN PRODUCTION VOLUMES

Another advantage of the CD-ROM is that the medium facilitates repeat production. When dealing with mask ROM, executives had to predict market trends three months ahead and predetermine production volume, but in practice it is impossible to make accurate predictions. They were constantly forced to make decisions under difficult circumstances. Says Tokunaka, "That's why we strongly believed that the PlayStation should be a format that would solve that problem for software house executives."

Repeat production was very difficult with mask ROM, but it wasn't an issue with CD-ROM. Because manufacturers could respond immediately to market demand, there was no need to carry excess inventory. This was the medium's greatest advantage. Namco Senior Managing Director Nakamura explains from the software producer's point of view: "With mask ROM, we had to deliver the master copy three months before the release date, but with CD-ROM the game would go on sale as scheduled if we delivered only a month beforehand. The content of the game would also be better, because the master copy would be that much improved. Production of replenishment stock takes only three days, so we don't incur any unnecessary inventory costs. It's a great help to us."

What better solution to their problems? The software houses had been released from making the crucial decision on production volume. The advantage of CD-ROM is that manufacturers need to produce only what the market needs. Production volume could be precisely controlled so that demand for one hundred copies could be met by additional production of exactly one hundred units. Unlike mask ROM, which is unsuited to repeat production, there is no need to produce extra in advance. CD-ROMs can be pressed in two days, so provided the printed sleeves are available, responding to small-lot orders is a simple matter.

Sony believed this should be the decisive factor, dramatically reducing the pressure felt by retailers as well as executives of game manufacturer. Retailers could simply order whatever software they needed from SCEI, whose distribution center was organized so it could deliver the following day if the title was in stock, and within six days if it wasn't. "We were trying to promote a business model based on an ordering system that responds immediately to sales trends and ensured that retailers didn't hold excess stock," Sato explains. "In the days of mask ROM, many retailers had large stocks that they didn't know what to do with. By creating a situation whereby a retailer knew that they sold five units the previous day and that we could deliver an order for even a single copy the following day, retailers would be able to judge for themselves how many copies they needed. We attracted a lot of attention, because we were proposing a totally new idea. People found it strange at first, but then they began to take us seriously."

ADAPTING THE RECORD BUSINESS MODEL TO THE GAME BUSINESS

Although other companies had adopted CD-ROM in the past, none had thought in quite this way. The idea of using a medium because it allows for repeat production and ensuring that production matches demand was unique. "It's a wholesale transfer of record industry know-how," says Sato. "We simply transplanted the record industry's business model to the computer game market." The music industry is characterized by small-lot production of a diverse range of items, and it therefore has developed expertise in how to respond quickly to demand. Sato adds, "This method of doing business was instinctive to us."

People with good instincts know how to take appropriate action without thinking. That's why when people suddenly find themselves with a successful product, they immediately spring into action. Ohga expresses his views on this: "I was involved in the standardization of the compact cassette and CD, and made both media commercially successful. We have the methodology to determine what aspects of a business we need to get right to guarantee success. We succeeded with the CD because Sony made both the hardware and the software. This method was repeated with the PlayStation. One of the reasons for the PlayStation's success lies in the fact that I also manage a record company. I am the chief executive of Sony Music. I was the one who recruited Maruyama and decided to make

CD-ROMs at our Shizuoka Plant. Several times I made the decision to stop music CD production and give priority to PlayStation disks. We asked some other companies to help us manufacture the music disks we couldn't make at the Shizuoka Plant. Although any plant of any CD maker can produce standard CDs, we couldn't ask other companies to produce PlayStation disks, which are black."

The business models for music CD and mask ROM are exact opposites. The music CD business model, adopted by the PlayStation, has the following features:

- Users select what they want from the many titles available.
- If a title is a hit, additional copies can be supplied quickly. Repeat production is possible.

By contrast, the Nintendo Super Famicom business model can be described as follows:

- Only a limited number of high-quality software is available.
- The nature of the medium does not allow repeat production.

The most effective expertise the computer game industry adapted from the record industry was the rational attitude that, in the words of Masashi Shimamoto (currently executive director and sales director of SCEI), "there's no need to make perfect demand forecasts. It's not really possible anyway. Since you can gear up for repeat production at any time, we can make more copies if a title sells well. Software is a business in which past experience is rarely a useful indicator."

Shimamoto came from a background in sales at Sony Music. He experienced a situation in which an artist who had released a hit album failed to do well with the next album. "One of my artists, Eiichi Otaki, released a hit album called *Long Vacation*. It sold 1.5 million copies. We thought he'd made it and estimated that his next album would sell at least 800,000 copies, or half as many as the previous album. We cut a million copies and managed to sell only 70,000. I've had many similar experiences. It's the same with the game industry; with the exception of a few well-known titles, it's impossible to predict demand in advance."

To take this argument to its extreme, there is no need to predict demand at all because repeat production is so easy with CD-ROM. Even if the initial release is small, the decision to increase production can be made after it becomes obvious that a title is going to sell. All that is needed is a system to quickly supply products as demand rises. "The greatest strength that we nurtured at Sony Music is the effective use of the CD repeat-production facilities," says Shimamoto. The PlayStation is a format that incorporates record company–style ideas in many areas, and CD repeat production is a typical example of "record company culture."

It could be argued that Sony's competitors, Sega and NEC in particular, did not come up with the same idea when they used CD-ROM because they did not have a resource like Sony Music close at hand. Moreover, those planning Sony's game distribution had been steeped in Sony Music culture through-out their careers, so it was inevitable for things to have moved in that direction. Indeed, any other approach would have been unnatural.

Sony has recently started to perfect the way it responds quickly to demand in repeat production. In the past, it had always released new titles on Fridays. This was an industry convention followed with the PlayStation, but beginning in July 1997 Sony started releasing new titles on Thursdays instead.

If a new title is released on a Friday, the product is delivered to retailers on Thursday and goes on sale on Friday morn-ing. Based on sales data at 1,500 retail stores, about a third of the total number nationwide, repeat orders are placed on Saturday. Sony Music's Shizuoka Plant would repeat production on Monday; the CDs were finished on Wednesday and delivered to stores on Thursday. In this case, however, orders had to be decided on the basis of only Friday's sales data; this meant that forecasts were at times inaccurate.

To estimate repeat-order volumes more accurately, Sony decided to start selling new titles on Thursdays so repeat orders could be estimated from the sales data for two days. Products that sold quickly from the day of launch and for which same-day repeat orders were placed could be manufactured as early as the following Tuesday. These could be dispatched on Wednesday and delivered to the retailer on the same day.

Some stores could not wait until Thursday and would start selling on Wednesday, a day earlier. This practice is called "flying selling" in Japan. Sony would caution retailers who did this, but at the same time did not forget to gather information by asking, "How's it selling?"

The key to repeat-production management is accuracy in predicting the initial production volume. Shimamoto has a story on this subject that he is proud to tell, about Capcom's Bio Hazard, which went on sale in March 1997. When Sony took advance orders from retailers, it came to a total of 120,000 copies. Shimamoto, however, was convinced that it would sell 200,000 copies. "My sales forecasts for records are rarely spot-on, but I had absolute confidence in Bio Hazard. I don't play computer games, so in that respect I'm a total amateur, but my children, gamers that I know, and student monitors all said, 'This game is really going to sell.' So I was convinced that it would be a hit."

He placed an order with the plant for 200,000 units, 80,000 more than the advance order figure. Bio Hazard went on sale on Friday, March 22. He received reports from monitor stores nationwide that the title was selling far more briskly than had been expected. It sold even more quickly over the next two days.

This is where the repeat-production performance comes into play. Replenishment stock was produced at the rate of 100,000 to 150,000 copies per week for many weeks, and the title became a runaway hit, eventually selling 1.2 million copies. Shimamoto asked Maruyama to telephone Sony Music's Shizuoka Plant and order manufacturing to give top priority to the production of Bio Hazard. Games took priority over music CDs, however busy the plant might have been. Shimamoto says: "We could work so quickly because we had our own plant. Since we started up the CD business, CDs have taken over our lives."

Things did not always go according to plan. Namco director Haraguchi recalls, "There were times when SCEI would say, 'This title is going to sell 500,000 copies,' but we wouldn't agree because our own data suggested that the best we could hope for was 300,000 copies. Our sales forecasts simply didn't agree, so initially we started with a lower production figure. On other occasions, Sony wouldn't accept our sales forecasts and insisted on a lower initial production figure."

THE "SELL DIRECT" CONCEPT

It was common knowledge in the industry that the failure of the Sega Saturn was the result of Sega's dependence on the long-established wholesaler organization Shoshinkai in spite of adopting CD-ROM as an innovative medium. Following the same argument, we can say that the reason for the PlayStation's success is that Sony revolutionized distribution in order to take advantage of the features of CD-ROM as a medium.

Sato explains: "The Shoshinkai wholesaler distribution system was created by Nintendo for the purpose of distributing mask ROM products. Our software titles are CD-ROM, so there was no need to hold large inventories and ongoing supply was possible. Given the circumstances, we thought we should set up a marketing system that took advantage of those features."

A legend about PlayStation frequently told at Sony goes like this: "There are two geniuses involved in the PlayStation, technologist Kutaragi and marketing expert Sato." Sony president Ohga describes Sato as follows: "We had Sato working at CBS Sony Records from its early days. I'm the one who made him responsible for marketing the PlayStation. He has done really well. Time after time, he put into action ideas that were unheard of in the computer-game industry. He did with the PlayStation the same thing he had done successfully at CBS Sony, taking a totally different approach from the traditional record industry model."

It was quite natural for Sato to use direct selling instead of going through wholesalers to maximize the benefits of CD-ROM. Says Sato: "In the software business, the dealer is the point of contact with the end user. In the store it's very important how the dealer responds to software trends. How a dealer replies to a customer who asks what a particular software title is about and how accurately the dealer communicates the product's selling points are absolutely crucial. Simply put, dealers must be able to answer correctly when a customer asks, 'When is that software that everyone is talking about going to be on sale?' For these reasons, direct selling to retailers is essential."

Sato was keenly aware that the retail store was the battleground of the software business. How could Sony ensure that a dealer responded appropriately to a customer who wandered into the store with no particular purpose? How could they set up a memorable encounter between customer and software in the store? Sato believed that the direct-selling method was the answer.

Sato speaks of his background: "I worked in many different departments at CBS Sony. The company frequently moved employees around. I worked on discovering new talent and video software rights. My longest stint was four years in sales promotion. In my final years there I was based in Yokohama, responsible for a sales office and the Treffort label. But then the label was combined with another and suddenly I had nothing to do. That's why I spent so much time playing games. Perhaps that's why I was assigned to the PlayStation project."

While working in the video software rights business, he gained some experience in researching retail stores. "I learned a lot from studying retailers. Frequently game stores start off as porn magazine stores, switch to adult video stores, and then start video rental. They later start selling Famicoms and end up as game stores. Games are not a product category designated by law for resale, so it is difficult for stores to secure popular products. The success of their business depends on securing a supply of products that will sell."

Even Sato's experience of being sold a "new" product that turned out to have been used helped him to formulate strategy. "Ideally manufacturers should sell their own products. If I ever plan a marketing policy for another new venture, I'm sure to go for direct selling again. The reason is speed. The direct- selling method is much faster than selling through a wholesaler in terms of information flow and supply logistics. What's happening on the front lines in the market? Which titles are selling, and how many copies? Only with direct sales can you respond quickly to the changing situation and make timely decisions on repeat production."

THE PURCHASE-FOR-RESALE MODEL: THE REAL REVOLUTION

Sato concentrated further on studying the characteristics of CD-ROM. What more could be done to maximize the strengths of a medium that facilitated repeat production? SCEI had already decided to sell its own hardware and software directly to retailers, but Sato felt something was still missing. He needed a decisive weapon to compete successfully with the huge regime that was thought to be in an unassailable position in the market.

One day in the spring of 1993, as Sato was mulling over these issues, things began to come into focus. SCEI employees were keenly aware of the benefits of CD-ROM. Sato was convinced that the company had the ability to utilize the strengths of the medium and, in response to market trends, deliver the number of CDs required. But he also wondered whether there were other problems that he needed to address. As we have seen, SCEI did not have the resources to produce good-quality software in-house, so in starting up the PlayStation platform it had to rely on third-party software producers.

At this stage, Sato imagined a nightmarish situation. Software producers have confidence in the titles that they make, and would understandably want to sell as many copies as possible. If a software house sold directly to retailers, it might pressure the stores to take a large number of copies all at once. Retailers would find themselves with a large inventory that would be difficult to dispose of. Meanwhile, smaller software houses without this kind of marketing ability would seek distribution via existing wholesalers, which might follow the same old practice of flooding the market with copies. If more copies hit the market than was justified by demand, they would remain unsold and prices would collapse. What distribution model was needed to prevent this outcome?

Sato continued to contemplate the situation. The problem lay in the industry's entrenched mask ROM–centered business format. The industry was filled with experts in managing a difficult medium such as mask ROM. It takes several months to produce mask ROM, so repeat production is impractical. For this reason, the industry had always followed the pattern of producing a large initial run and unloading any excess product in the used-software market. Selling overrun software bundled with more popular titles and hoarding popular titles for sale at a premium were commonplace. As Sato toured the market, he found the shadow cast by mask ROM to be incredibly large.

What would happen if Sony released its vulnerable CD-ROM medium in a world ravaged by demons? There was a strong possibility that before the company could take advantage of the repeat-production capabilities characteristic of CD-ROM, the titles would be treated in the same way as mask ROM and the market would remain turbulent. Whether software industry people accustomed to the mask ROM business (having to carry a large inventory to secure a supply of popular titles due to production complications) would understand the advantages of CD-ROM was not known. Even though the medium has excellent characteristics, the situation in the industry would remain unchanged if those handling the distribution continued with the established approach.

Old habits die hard. Although the industry may understand the benefits of the new system, people's actions are ruled by custom and emotions. Surely, software houses would be anxious and insist on producing as many copies of the new titles as possible.

Sato was desperate. He felt that if the situation could not be changed, there would be no point in going ahead with the PlayStation project. He recalls: "I began to think that instead of leaving the distribution to others we should do it ourselves. It would take a long time for people so accustomed to the mask ROM business model to learn the advantages of CD-ROM. If that were to be the case, we would have to do all the marketing during this period. It seemed to be our duty to ensure that the repeat-supply aspect of the business worked smoothly."

Soon Sato had devised a totally new distribution method called the "purchase-for-resale" method. He explained to the software houses: "You leave the selling to us, and in return we'll provide the fastest response to demand in the business." SCEI, the platform developer, functions as a wholesaler that purchases products from software houses and resells them to retailers. The key feature of this approach to distribution is that SCEI, not the software house, is responsible for making adjustments between production (initial and repeat production volumes) and inventory.

Sato explains: "The strength of CD-ROM as a medium lies in its suitability for fast repeat production. Given that, surely it makes sense to adapt the selling approach to the medium. The purchase-for-resale system allows the quickest possible response to market trends. Repeat production made possible by the use of CD-ROM was a totally new business format, used by no other company. We had to devise ways to ensure that this format would be widely accepted in the industry, because we would be the only company doing it."

Sony's goal was a quick turnaround of repeat orders for best-selling titles to ensure a balance between production and inventory. SCEI would do all the marketing in a standardized way to prevent dealer loading and inventory problems. To be more precise, the software house and SCEI would each have a role: The developer would be responsible for sales promotion and SCEI responsible for the actual selling and distribution. SCEI also decided to take the initiative, after consultation with the software houses, in deciding initial and repeat production volume. Sato explains: "This was the result of fundamental questioning of the traditional distribution system, in which used software had become a crucial mechanism for normalizing distribution."

It was also a way to demonstrate by example the advantages of CD-ROM. It would make software houses steeped in traditional practices understand how the CD-ROM repeat business works. Doing nothing might result in the software producers reverting to their old ways, so SCEI would take the initiative and propose a different method. SCEI established the system to operate for a limited, predetermined period of time.

Some in the company questioned why a platform developer had to go this far, but Sato insisted. To manage repeat business accurate market information on hardware sales is essential, because software will not sell in higher numbers than hardware shipments. Producing 500,000 copies of a title when only 300,000 units of hardware have been sold instantly results in 200,000 units of surplus stock. Hardware makers need to keep track of software trends, and software houses need to monitor hardware sales figures. The solution that satisfied both requirements was for SCEI, the hardware maker, to sell all third-party software as well. Being a hardware manufacturer, SCEI would of course know how many units it had produced and would produce in the future. Moreover, under Sato's software-distribution system, all of the software for the PlayStation would be produced at Sony Music's Shizuoka Plant, which would enable SCEI to track software production as well.

GETTING SMALL DEVELOPERS TO PARTICIPATE

Sato had a number of goals for his new purchase-for-resale system. Indeed, this system was the most important issue that had to be addressed in launching the PlayStation. It would become a powerful weapon in increasing the number of software producers participating in the PlayStation platform. Sato thought it was a good way, for example, to attract smaller software houses that are technically brilliant, but may not have the wherewithal

for visiting dealers to sell their products directly. These companies had had to rely on the established wholesaler organization
to sell their products, and usually they were not given the same
respect that the larger ones got.

Sato says: "We wanted to enable small software houses
that had no time for selling to produce excellent titles for us.
How could we persuade them to make software for us? I
resolved to do the selling for them in place of the Shoshinkai
network, however difficult it might be, because if they would
produce software for us, it would be worth the effort." This was
a line of thinking similar to providing a library to creators so
they could concentrate on producing a title without having to
do complicated preliminary development work.

When Sato proposed this idea at SCEI, a heated debate
ensued. Could SCEI really succeed in being a wholesaler?
Could the business be made to work on a profit margin of a few
percent, considering the selling costs? Would a small team be
able to handle a large volume of business? Would they manage
to benefit from economies of scale?

Most important to Sato was developing a way to track
hardware and software sales in real time. Highly accurate sales
figures were needed to adjust supply to demand. The record-
industry experience within SCEI became useful at this point.
Maruyama says: "Those in the record industry have many
years of experience in managing the relationship between market trends, inventory, and production, so we can judge the volume of repeat production needed for a given rate of sales."

Sato took special care to ensure that excess supply would
not occur. "If mountains of PlayStation consoles and software
were on display in stores, the implication would be that they're
not selling, that they are in oversupply. So we needed to track
accurately how they were selling." So every Saturday and Sunday was devoted to thoroughly investigating how the hardware

and software were selling. Armed with a list of sampling techniques, the team toured retailers to conduct point-of-sale surveys that identified sales trends. Using the information from these surveys, SCEI was able to produce just enough stock to cover shortages.

"IT WILL NEVER WORK!"

Unfortunately, the software houses were not easily won over to a system that involved SCEI taking over their independent distribution efforts. Objections took many forms: Some houses wanted to continue selling through wholesalers. Some claimed that they had the clout to use their own sales reps to sell directly to retailers. Some stubbornly demanded to know why they should not sell their own titles.

Sato, however, was resolute: "There's some opposition, but we must follow this method." If distribution via wholesalers occurred alongside SCEI's system, even on a small scale, there could be conflict. And iIf SCEI failed to adopt stock purchase for resale and allowed each software producer to handle its own distribution, many of them wouldn't be able to visit dealers directly to sell their titles. This meant they would fall back on wholesalers. A situation would result in which a medium such as CD-ROM would be sold via wholesalers, which are slow to pass on information. Meanwhile, software houses that realized the advantages of CD-ROM repeat production would try to maximize the benefit. In effect, there would be two competing distribution systems.

The retailer would also have problems: Different distributors would deliver software for the same PlayStation platform, resulting in complicated sales voucher administration. The store would be able to track sales volume accurately on titles supplied by SCEI, but volume data for products obtained from other sources would be suspect, and the decision to produce replacement stock could either be delayed or based on inaccurate figures. Sato was determined to prevent such a complicated situation from taking shape.

Tokunaka comments: "They say ignorance is bliss. We had no track record in the industry, so we didn't have any ties or obligations either. You can't do anything new if you worry about what the wholesalers will think. My experience with starting up CBS Sony taught me that you have to confront this situation when embarking on a new business. There's no point in starting a new business without achieving innovation."

In stark contrast to Sony, whose ideas for every aspect of the PlayStation business suited the new medium of CD-ROM, Sega used CD-ROM but opted for traditional distribution via wholesalers. It was a choice resulting from Sega's failure to think through the repeat-production advantages of CD-ROM. Later on, as SCEI's approach to distribution gradually became evident, Sega was unable to change its system. One reason was its relationship with the wholesaler community: Sega was unable to simply sever its ties with wholesalers it had been doing business with for a long time. Although the company understood the problems inherent in its approach and had learned the benefits of CD-ROM repeat production, it was not ruthless enough to stop dealing with wholesalers. The difference between Sony and Sega lay in whether or not they had something to give up in the first place.

Many top executives of software houses objected to SCEI's distribution system simply because it was unprecedented. Although they were offered various incentives, they initially couldn't see how the purchase-for-resale system could work to their advantage. SCEI would have been readily accepted had it fallen in with the traditional distribution method, but a new company employing a new marketing method was too strange in an industry accustomed to tried-and-true business practices. "Even I was astounded by what we had dreamed up," confesses Shimamoto. "The software producers kept telling me, 'It will never work.'"

Shimamoto, who had been responsible for selling to record stores at Sony Music, joined SCEI in January 1991, immediately after the company was established. He was called into the office of Mr. Ozawa, then president of Sony Music, and asked whether he played computer games.

"No, I don't," replied Shimamoto.

"Well, then, you should give it a try. I'd like you to move to SCEI and handle sales."

Shimamoto, who imagined that his new job would be visiting retailers, was astounded to learn that he would also be responsible for purchase-for-resale liaison with software producers. By then the details of the stock-purchase sales method were close to being finalized. He recalls: "This method wasn't directly inherited from Sony Music. It's an idea that Mr. Sato thought up, so I was surprised to learn we were doing something like this. Sale on consignment, a method similar to purchase for resale, is common in the record industry, but Sony Music was unusual in that it refused consignment arrangements. The argument was that nobody would make a serious effort to sell products which belonged to someone else."

Although Shimamoto visited many software houses in an effort to persuade them that the purchase-for-resale system was a good idea, few were willing to sign an agreement. Winning them over would require several additional calls. At times he would brood, because his work was such a struggle—and he didn't particularly like games in the first place. Although he knew that the purchase-for-resale system was unattractive to companies that wanted to do their own selling, he persevered. He strongly believed that the wholesaler-distribution system must not continue unchallenged.

Opposition was particularly strong from the leading software houses. This was no surprise: They would be stripped of their freedom to sell their own titles. They had to consult with SCEI before deciding on initial production volume. Their marketing staffs felt threatened because they believed their jobs were being taken away. Shimamoto tried to persuade these software houses using the appeal of repeat production: "Apart from titles that we know are going to sell well, let's start off small and nurture titles into big sellers. If we take the title through several cycles of repeat production, we can achieve strong sales figures." But the reaction to his words was always the same: "We don't want to hear that. We want you to make a big splash right from the beginning, even if only with our software."

Software houses were also skeptical about SCEI's plans with respect to the retail market. The Shoshinkai distributed software to 25,000 outlets—game and record stores—so from the software producer's point of view, its products had broad distribution, although this was questionable. By contrast, according to Shimamoto, SCEI wanted to limit supply to five thousand stores. "Is that all? That's far fewer than before" was the usual response. Shimamoto says, "There are seven to eight thousand record stores in Japan, so I was confident that five thousand was about the right scale for a software business."

Assuming a turnover of $100,000 and up per store per month, the size of the record market, comprising seven to eight thousand stores, would be around $1 billion dollars. If the figure of 25,000 outlets was accurate, Shimamoto knew, the turnover at each store had to be low—hence his five-thousand-store initial target. "But because we were starting from scratch, even five thousand was too many. My personal initial estimate was about one thousand stores, but when I said that to software developers, they would become furious," he confesses.

Nevertheless, as he continued in his efforts to sign up software houses, he found a few people who were sympathetic to his views. He began to get some positive responses to the persuasive sales pitch "If you use the purchase-for-resale system, it will be much easier to ascertain the maximum number that a title is likely to sell than with the current approach." He would continue: "We need produce no more software than is justified by current sales. To do this we have to stay on top of sales trends, and we need to purchase your products and sell them on to make this possible."

The power of the Sony name was also effective. One of the roles of a wholesaler is to maintain credit, and in the words of one software producer, "it goes without saying that Sony has a much better credit standing than the Shoshinkai wholesalers."

OPPOSITION FROM KONAMI

The software developer Konami remained stubbornly opposed to purchase for resale. The company had a strong direct selling tradition and believed firmly in selling its own products. Says Managing Director Kitagami: "We believed that the Sony format would be the engine of next-generation game machines. We also had faith in the Sony brand. Eventually, we decided to participate in the Sony format. At the time, we were making software for the Super Famicom and Sega Megadrive, but the market for both products was saturated and there was little potential for growth. We had to think about the next core platform. Sega always secures its own position before calling on third-party developers, so at that point in time Sony was our only hope."

Talks had gone smoothly and Konami was on the verge of deciding to participate in the PlayStation platform, but the company balked when the purchase-for-resale system was mentioned. A stalemate ensued. Konami is well known for its own sales network covering all areas of Japan—its approach is dubbed "capillary selling" by people in the industry. At the time, Konami had a hundred sales offices and thirteen sales companies nationwide, a more powerful network than that of SCEI.

Konami was quickly expanding its sales organization for home-use games. It was able to build its own sales network because it had originally allocated a large number of employees to sales and maintenance of arcade games, and these employees could now also get involved with sales of software for home-use games. Kitagami explains: "We're a manufacturer, so the obvious thing is for us to have our own sales network. It's a manufacturer's duty to develop products by understanding user needs, and for that a direct sales network is essential. Makers should not leave distribution to others. With CD-ROM, which involves quick repeat production that simply isn't possible with mask ROM cartridges, we felt we should sell directly."

Konami's view clashed completely with SCEI's policy of purchasing and reselling all the software. Kitagami says: "I didn't like it at all when we were told that we wouldn't be selling our own software, but that SCEI would purchase it for resale. This was a rare opportunity for us to break away from the Shoshinkai and take charge of our own distribution, but SCEI was going to assume control instead."

Shimamoto made a valiant effort to persuade Konami, but the company did not relent easily. After many visits from Shimamoto, however, Konami gave in to his persistence and reluctantly agreed to SCEI's terms—but on the condition that the agreement would be for a limited period. Says Kitagami: "We offered to cooperate with SCEI's purchase for resale system for a year and a half and no longer."

The two companies agreed on the following terms: For eighteen months after the PlayStation's release, SCEI would sell Konami products via its own sales network. During that time Konami would improve its own direct sales network and take over its own distribution from SCEI at the end of the eighteen-month period. From December 1994 to 1996, Konami products were sold through the SCEI sales network as stipulated in the agreement. Kitagami was not always pleased with how the situation was developing. He kept a close eye on how Konami products were handled, and often stormed into SCEI in a rage.

"SCEI makes the final decision on the shipment volume for the launch day, but the fact is, whether that figure is large or small isn't all that important, because with CD-ROM you can increase the supply volume by repeat production. The problem was that a title would sell well and stores would go out of stock. This would happen even though I'd told SCEI staff to make sure retailers wouldn't run out of a certain title, because we knew it might sell out. When something like this happens, I get angry and demand to know what on earth they think they're doing. It's easy enough to say you can produce more in three days, but those three days could make the difference between success and failure. I complained to SECI as an executive of a software house, for whom retail sales are everything."

The eighteen-month period passed, and Konami notified SCEI in 1996 that it would sell its own products from that time forward as stipulated in the agreement. Says Kitagami, "But they wouldn't return the software right away. Mr. Maruyama and Mr. Shimamoto kept making excuses and tried to delay returning the titles. I was furious. It was all laid out in the agreement, so we were determined to proceed as had been agreed. I told them that we had steadily made preparations to begin direct sales in the way SCEI had requested, and the system was ready and waiting."

Kitagami says SCEI eventually returned Konami's products, but reluctantly. From Konami's point of view, it was only doing what had been agreed with SCEI. However, Shimamoto contradicts Kitagami's story: "I don't think that's true. We returned the titles without delay."

In any event, SCEI considered purchase for resale as an interim measure until the repeat-production advantages of CD-ROM became established in the industry and distribution was normalized. It had no objection to a company with an effective distribution system beginning to sell its own products. Sato says, "If a company has a well-established approach to distribution, there is no need for us to buy their products from them for resale. And we have no intention of forcing our system on such companies."

Indeed, SCEI's attitude began to soften in certain respects. In June 1997, the company changed its policy of deciding the initial volume of a newly released title in consultation with the software house, giving developers the right to make the decision. This came in response to demands by some software companies that the policy be changed.

Software houses' views on direct selling were mixed, however. Kitagami of Konami appealed to Namco: "Large software producers should sell direct. Namco, in particular, has so many sales offices it should be able to sell direct without depending on Sony. Please change to selling direct. We feel like Konami is the odd one out." But Namco director Haraguchi replied firmly, "We don't sell direct." He elaborates: "A salesperson using high-pressure tactics to push his products won't succeed. An unsuccessful product won't sell, whatever approach you may adopt. Forcing stores to take on software titles that don't sell will only backfire, causing damage to your brand image. I think SCEI's purchase-for-resale system is fair."

Haraguchi could be positive about SCEI's system because he was confident that he was keeping track of the latest market trends. "Namco doesn't cede full responsibility for distribution to Sony. We have fifteen store-development staffers who keep in close contact with one thousand retail outlets nationwide. We conduct our own focused sales promotion activities. And because we compile our own information, we have data on how many orders we are getting for our software. So we can discuss things with Sony's sales staff armed with our own data."

Namco is able to cover its nationwide retail network with just fifteen people because it produces only a small number of titles, roughly one per month, and has no sales offices of its own. Says Haraguchi: "At present we feel that SCEI's method is the best. It's more efficient for a single company to take over sales activities, instead of each manufacturer selling direct and following its own approach. It's not the selling method that sells products, but the content of the game and how it is promoted.

Konami, by contrast, produces many titles. Because of this high volume, selling direct is a viable option for the company.

THE "NO REBATE" CONTROVERSY

SCEI continued to cause a sensation in the industry with its extraordinary proposals, and never was this more true than when it began to look for new retail outlets. Says Shimamoto: "The one channel we didn't develop aggressively was record stores. In fact, nobody suggested that we should focus our network on record stores simply because Sony Music was experienced in dealing with them. We had learned at Sony Music that there is a world of difference in the way stores treat main products and secondary products. For this reason, record stores never became a main sales route."

Shimamoto had learned this lesson from Sony's attempt to sell video software at record stores—a distribution channel well known to the company. The attempt failed dismally. The videos simply did not sell. A music store's mainstay products are music CDs, and most such stores have little interest in videos. Likewise with consumer electronics stores, where video software is considered a peripheral product that accompanies the hardware and not as a business in its own right. (One exception to this rule was Matsushita Electric, whose principal sales outlets for 3-DO were consumer electronics stores.)

Which outlets did SCEI target? Game stores. The company focused on one store for each area with a population of 30,000 to 40,000. In the words of Shimamoto: "We approached stores in the region starting with the ones with the highest sales. We visited each store and asked them to stock our products."

Large discount stores presented a problem. SCEI began signing agreements with retail stores in July 1994, but few large stores were interested. In most cases, the two sides could not agree on terms and conditions. Large stores always demanded a rebate, wanting favorable terms in exchange for selling high volume. Shimamoto would reply, pretending ignorance: "What do you mean? Isn't the discount the same nationwide? What do you mean by a rebate? Could you please elaborate? You see, we are inexperienced in this business. . . ."

Of course, this was a deliberate ploy. SCEI wanted to offer the same terms to all retailers. It was commonly accepted in the industry that the traditional distribution chaos was caused by rebates. In the record industry, on the other hand, large and small stores were all treated equally. A creative work like a record cannot be replaced by a different work; they are "one and only" products that cannot be obtained from other sources. Therefore, it doesn't make sense to offer different terms to stores selling this type of product. SCEI wanted to offer the same terms to small, local stores and big discount stores, but time passed as retailers failed to appreciate the benefits of its bold no-rebate policy. SCEI finally reached an agreement with Yodobashi Camera, one of Japan's largest discount stores, on November 20, just two weeks before the PlayStation went on sale.

As a launch date approaches, there is a lot of media coverage. Merchants have a natural instinct for identifying products that are likely to enjoy huge sales. Any savvy businessperson, upon hearing the purchase terms, would conclude that the PlayStation was an opportunity not to be missed. Shimamoto explains: "We referred to the figures on records and consumer electronics products when we decided on the discount to offer the retail store. It's 30 percent off list for records and 25 percent for video software. We decided on 25 percent for game software because it's a visual product. We referred to wholesale prices of consumer electronics products in deciding the hardware discount. There is a complex rebate system for consumer electronics goods, but ignoring that, the wholesale discount was 25 to 30 percent of the list price. So we decided to take the lower figure and offer retailers a 25 percent discount on hardware."

However, in the game-machine industry it was customary for the discount on hardware to be 10 percent to 15 percent of the retail price—a very modest discount. This was a reflection of the principle that companies make money on software, not hardware. Shimamoto was not aware of this. "Being new to the business, I had no idea the discount was so low," he confesses.

This meant that on a product with a recommended retail price of $399, the retailer's margin is just 10 percent, or $39.90. With the PlayStation, however, the retailer would receive a 25 percent margin, or $100. Retailers are rarely offered such favorable terms.

Furthermore, with so much media exposure it seemed certain that the PlayStation would sell very quickly from day one. Yodobashi Camera and other discounters decided that it would be better under these circumstances to forget minor differences about the terms of the agreement and get on the bandwagon. In effect, the PlayStation was being shipped to retailers with a $100 bill attached to it. A president of a discount store in Akihabara telephoned SCEI to say, "Thank you very much indeed. We made a huge profit."

When the retail price was subsequently reduced, the percentage was adjusted on the grounds that it was too favorable to the retailer. Shimamoto says sheepishly: "We were really naïve. There was so much we had to learn."

Still, it is surely true that the PlayStation is what it is today because full advantage was taken of an amateur's approach. To this day, SCEI does not offer volume discounts, nor will it extend an additional discount to retailers that purchase in volume.

AD CAMPAIGN BORROWED FROM THE 8MM VIDEO CONCEPT

The PlayStation project saw innovation after innovation, and SCEI's advertising strategy was no exception. The method by which the company elicited interest in the product was a veritable revolution in user–manufacturer communications. Says Akira Sato: "Video games are almost like movies as a business. It's essential to consider how to generate attention prior to the launch date, and how to achieve your initial target on the launch day. It is definitely a promotion business in that everything depends on how you appeal to the end user."

Treating the game business as a promotion business was indeed a fresh approach: The PlayStation launch marked the first time that the business was defined in this way. SCEI saw the key to the PlayStation's success, then, as implementing the promotional concepts effectively. An example is the unusual campaign conducted during the run-up to the December 3, 1994, launch date.

Why did Sony choose that date? December 3, 1994, was a Saturday. It was the first time a game format would be launched on a Saturday—Friday was the traditional day for product releases. But SCEI was not simply out to make a break with tradition. Says Masatsuka Saeki, who was in charge of advertising strategy: "December is a busy season, so it had to go on sale during the first week of the month. It was the only date that was suitable."

Information about the coming of PlayStation had already reached core game users, who wanted to know just two things: the price and the launch date. The main purpose of the advertising campaign, therefore, would be to create a lasting impression of the release date. Hakuhodo, SCEI's ad agency, suggested: "If we could make the date 1-2-3 [12/3, or December 3], you could use some novel communications copy." Maruyama thought it was a great idea, and that date was chosen.

SCEI's initial target was the core game-user group. According to Saeki: "If all core users bought the PlayStation, it would immediately become a platform several hundred thousand users strong. We were more interested in attracting a million or so occasional users, thinking this would be the mark of a major success. But occasional users are strongly influenced by core users." For this reason, it was important to target core users first.

The information communicated in advertisements had to be precise. For example, Saeki deliberately reminded the media of Sega whenever he was interviewed: "By then, 3-DO was obviously failing, and there were rumors that the market for home-use game machines was in decline. So I decided to tell interesting stories to grab the attention of the reporters, and always mentioned the name of Sega as a competitor." The strategy was to have as many column inches as possible devoted to Sony in a "Sony vs. Sega" saga. The media love stories of competing companies battling it out, and the Sega Saturn was scheduled to go on sale Friday, December 22, about three weeks following the PlayStation debut. Targeting this date, SCEI began an advertising campaign announcing the PlayStation's debut.

The advertising copy went as follows: "Wait for December 3. The PlayStation will change the world of games like one, two, three," a play on the date December 3 (12/3). It was an effective teaser, a classic advertising technique that hides the focus of the ad to pique user interest. Saeki had used a similar technique when he was at Sony working on product planning for audio accessories. Until then, he had been made to work on nothing but little-known products and was disenchanted with his job. So he responded to an internal recruitment announcement and transferred to the advertising department on January 8, 1985, the day the first 8mm video CCD-V8 was launched.

One of Saeki's major coups—one still talked about at Sony to this day—was the promotion campaign for the CCD-TR55 in 1989. The CCD-TR55, the first passport-size video camera, was responsible for reversing Sony's fortunes in the 8mm video format, which lagged behind the VHS-C format of Victor, a Sony competitor.

When Saeki first saw the TR55 in March 1989, he decided on an advertising strategy that emphasized teasers. "I thought that a teaser was the only way to go because I knew the product would sell," says Saeki. Teaser TV commercials were aired in a major ad campaign between May 31, the date the launch was announced in the press, and the June 31 launch date. The commercial featured Atsuko Asano at an airport holding an object wrapped in a white cloth and shouting, "A new handycam goes on sale soon. It's called. . . ." At that moment, a jet aircraft flies past behind her and her voice is drowned out by the engine noise.

The teaser strategy was adopted in other areas as well. For example, retail stores cooperated in the strategy: They did not complain when the product was not delivered until the morning of the launch date, even though the custom was to deliver it three days earlier.

On the morning of June 21, shipments were made to retailers across Japan. Saeki recalls, "I was really surprised. I went to Akihabara in the morning to see what was happening and saw a long line of customers waiting. I was deeply impressed that people were lining up to buy a product with a price tag of over $2,000."

After his success with the TR55, Saeki joined the PlayStation project. On November 1, 1993, Nobuyuki Idei, at the time responsible for advertising at Sony, alerted Saeki to an impending change.

"Saeki. You're about to be transferred."

"Oh, no! Where to?"

"Planning department, domestic sales division."

"That sounds . . . pretty boring."

"Well, then, how about this other team?. . ." suggested Idei, then told Saeki about the PlayStation business preparation group. When Saeki said during an interview with Akira Sato that his specialty was advertising, the response was a cool "Really? Advertising? Is *that* what you want to do?" Saeki was angered by his tone, which implied that advertising was unimportant work.

The strategy for the PlayStation launch was modeled on that of the TR55. Saeki says, "Without my experience with the TR55, I couldn't have managed the PlayStation's debut strategy." The experience with the TR55 to which Saeki refers entailed spending billions of yen on advertising. Sony spent ¥5 billion (about $50 million) in six months on the 8mm video campaign. A nationwide TV spot costs $4 to $5 million. A nationwide newspaper ad campaign costs $7 to $8 million. Spending money on this scale is not something to be attempted

casually, and effectively allocating advertising budgets to different media is a tricky task for someone without experience. Saeki
acquired a sense of when to adopt a tease strategy. He learned
the importance of knowing whether the conditions that make a
tease campaign appropriate exist with the product in question.

First of all, the product category must be widely known
and one in which consumers are interested. However innovative a product, if the product category is brand-new, tease
advertising will not generate user interest. At the time of its
release, the TR55 was very much in the news because the next-
generation video war between the VHS-C format and the 8mm
format had attracted a great deal of public attention.

The second condition is that the product must be a good
one. Because the advertising is provocative, the product must
live up to expectations once people learn what it is about. Disappointing the public only leads to loss of credibility, so the
product has to be regarded as innovative enough to justify hype.

Third, the company has to guarantee product delivery. It
has to ensure sufficient supply in the event the advertising is
effective and people rush to stores to buy the product.

"We were very anxious when the TR55 came out. We prepared to the point that we worried that we'd made too many of
them and there would be a surplus. From past experience of AV
products, it seemed unlikely that we could sell as many units as
we'd made at a price exceeding $2,000." However, the TR55,
which went on sale on June 21, 1989, sold out in just one week.

The PlayStation satisfied the first condition of being a
focus of attention. Articles about the battle among manufacturers to produce the next-generation game machine filled newspapers and magazines, and the subject was extensively
discussed by the general public as well. SCEI had announced
the PlayStation format to the media on May 10, and the design
prototype had also been made public. Matsushita's 3-DO was

also attracting considerable interest. In Saeki's words, "The PlayStation perfectly fulfilled the condition that it was an area that users knew a great deal about."

The second factor was the PlayStation itself. Saeki trusted Kutaragi concerning the hardware and had no concerns about that side of the business, but he was worried about the software. Would there be a selection of good software in time for the launch date? Since this was a concern for the whole company, from an advertising perspective he had to assume that the software would be ready on time and base his advertising plan on that assumption.

Third was the question of supply. In July 1994, no decision had been made about how many units would be available on the launch date. Although Saeki had Nintendo's history as a guide, he couldn't visualize how strong the PlayStation's attraction would be. He had no idea how many units would sell on the day of the launch. Although the 3-DO was also a home game machine, the situation with that product was so different that it did not serve as a useful guide. Saeki decided that the TR55 was a better reference point in this respect.

"During the course of our discussions, we somehow arrived at the consensus that it would be great if we could sell 300,000 units in the first month. That meant selling 100,000 units on the first day. It was only a rough guess, though," Saeki says. In practice, it was all the team could do to prepare 100,000 units for the launch day and 300,000 units for the first month. Everyone at SCEI worked as one to prepare for a launch of this magnitude.

ONLY PLAYSTATION WAS SUITABLE FOR FORMAT ADVERTISING

The "1-2-3" start-up campaign was successful. The company did in fact sell 100,000 units on the first day. Saeki recalls: "We didn't know until the day before launch whether core game users would line up outside stores on December 3. But when the day arrived, people formed lines in an atmosphere of tremendous excitement. The memory is still fresh in my mind."

Once the business had taken off, SCEI used one advertising stratagem after another. The company had unshakable faith in the notion that the PlayStation was a game platform appropriate for a format ad strategy.

Nintendo's advertising approach had been to stress that theirs was the best software available at the time. This is a valid approach to advertising in the game business, but SCEI did not follow Nintendo's example. PlayStation ads focused on the current status of the format, informing users about development activity that was under way and about the direction the format was going. Saeki explains: "In other words, the ads reflected our management policy. The most important thing with this type of advertising is that management decisions must be the right ones. Format ads will succeed only under those circumstances."

PlayStation's launch was successful for many reasons. One of them was that SCEI consistently used format ads to attract attention and create the impetus necessary for expanding the PlayStation user base. The advertising copy used from December 3 to December 20 read: "All games gather here." This was a clear announcement that the PlayStation was not a multimedia machine, as the 3-DO claimed to be, but rather a specialty game machine only. Although SCEI was a newcomer to the game industry, it was declaring that the PlayStation would be the machine on which many future games would be played.

A PlayStation format ad talked about even today is the "We'll hit a million units!" commercial run in the spring of 1995. It attracted a great deal of attention, because it made people wonder what it was about and at whom it was targeted. It made no difference to the average user whether SCEI sold a million PlayStations or not; nor did the ad do anything to communicate how interesting the games were.

Even within SCEI, some questioned the need to make sales goals public knowledge.

In fact, the ad campaign had a highly strategic aim. It was targeted at core users, many of whom had seen a platform or its software simply disappear from the market. The slogan "We'll hit a million units!" communicated the message that PlayStation would not suffer a similar fate. At the time of the campaign, 880,000 consoles had been sold, and SCEI wanted to drive home the fact that the PlayStation had become a serious player in the market.

Saeki had another reason for backing this ad campaign. Two months earlier, he had read an interview of Nintendo president Hiroshi Yamauchi in the October 18, 1994, issue of the newspaper *Nihon Keizai Shinbun*. The article contained the following passage: "To the reporter's question of whether Nintendo felt threatened by the 32-bit machines being released by Sega and Sony at the end of the year, Yamauchi replied, 'There are 300,000 to 400,000 game aficionados in Japan. Sega and Sony's next-generation machines will sell somewhere around that figure. But Matsushita's 3-DO Real hasn't achieved its initial sales target. I think it's unlikely that Sega and Sony will succeed in a business at which Matsushita failed. Most users will not spend 30,000 to 40,000 yen on a 32-bit game machine. By next summer the 32-bit market will have disappeared.'"

In anger, Saeki crumpled the newspaper into a ball, threw it on the floor, and exclaimed: "We'll show him! Not only will we sell 300,000 units, we'll sell a million. And before next summer, when he claims the business will have failed!"

Yamauchi had not been deliberately provocative. He had always claimed that no company other than Nintendo could succeed in the game market, and he meant what he said during the newspaper interview. But from Saeki's point of view—indeed, that of all SCEI employees—this was a challenge. It was tantamount to Yamauchi providing them with a sales target.

Clearly, the article provided the impetus for the "We'll hit a million units!" campaign. Many core users regard sales of hardware as a guide to whether or not a platform has staying power, and are hence sensitive to claims such as Yamauchi's. Seen in this light, the "We'll hit a million units!" campaign was significant. SCEI launched the campaign in March 1995, three months before "next summer" arrived.

THE REASON FOR "NO-COMPROMISE SERVICE"

The "No-Compromise Service" campaign of the summer of 1996 provided unmistakable evidence that the ad campaign masterminded by Saeki had in fact boosted PlayStation sales. SCEI reduced the price of the hardware by $100 to $299 and rereleased eight popular software titles under the slogan "PlayStation—The Best Series" at less than half the original price. Users were impressed with the company's promise of "No-Compromise Service," which was demonstrated by gestures such as lengthening the controller cord from 1.2 meters to 2 meters in response to complaints.

The "No-Compromise Service" slogan was chosen after considerable deliberation. In fact, as a slogan it was the company's second choice. The most popular proposal had been "Feeling Refreshed—PlayStation," an expression of the relief among SCEI staff that they had finally been able to respond to the demands of software houses.

As we have seen, early on SCEI had been responsible for making the final decision as to how many copies of a new software title should be pressed. Some software houses, however, had become increasingly dissatisfied at not being able to determine the volume of their own products. The problem was resolved in May 1996, when software producers were given the right to decide the size of a tile's first production run. A long-standing problem had been solved.

There was some concern, however, that the slogan "Feeling Refreshed" would expose the company's marketing mindset and internal politics to too great a degree. Saeki says: "I thought so, too. Choosing between the two slogans was a very difficult decision to make." After two weeks of deliberation, the company opted for "No-Compromise Service."

It would prove to be an excellent choice. Sales increased sharply after a commercial containing the slogan appeared on TV. To that point a total of 5 million consoles had been sold, but from then on, sales took off at a phenomenal pace. Square's (a game software developer) announcement shortly afterward that with its major hit Final Fantasy it was switching platforms from the N64—Nintendo's next-generation game machine— to the PlayStation, also had a major impact on sales.

Saeki is convinced that "No-Compromise Service" is what turned the tide. He says: "People liked it because it made sense. However clever an ad may be, it won't work unless it tells a good story. 'No-Compromise Service' made the biggest contribution to the company. After the ads came out, our serious-minded president, Tokunaka, became the center of attention every time he went out drinking in the evening and announced that he was the PlayStation president." The ad was clearly having an impact.

The April 1997 advertising campaign was an unusual one for a game machine. It involved eccentric slogans like "PlayStation is for good kids and good grown-ups"; "Beware of playing games for too long. Decide on a schedule and keep to it"; "Save up and buy software"; and " Take care not to eat too much watermelon." By this point, the game-machine war had been decided and the PlayStation was inarguably the most prominent of the three platforms. The purpose of the ads was to communicate the news that PlayStation had won the format war and to inform users of the status of the platform. However, Sony's sense of propriety dictated against saying so directly.

So the company ran advertisements atypical of game ads. "You see, we couldn't say such things if we weren't confident," Saeki remarks. Ironically, "Beware of playing games for too long" was well received by parents, who would say to their children, "Look. It's you that they're talking about!" It also struck a chord with core users, who would ask themselves, "I wonder if they're referring to me?"

ADVERTISE ONLY IF THE PRODUCT IS INTERESTING

The power of advertising was demonstrated again during the year-end campaign of 1997. The recession in Japan had spread to the game industry, and the traditional year-end surge in sales had failed to materialize even by the second half of November. The price of hardware had decreased to below $200, but demand was sluggish. PlayStation ads directly proposed giving the game as a gift, as expressed in the "A PlayStation Is Your Reward" campaign, which touted the game as a gift for deserving children. The campaign caused sales of the PlayStation to bounce back to tens of thousands of units per week.

The spring 1998 advertising campaign made a big contribution to software sales. Although it was a basic policy of SCEI not to advertise software, the company occasionally advertised a specific title that was likely to increase sales of hardware. The title chosen to spearhead the spring campaign was Tsurido, a fishing game. The Dual Shock Controller, a game controller equipped with a vibrating stick, had gone on sale in the fall of

1997, and Tsurido was the ideal game to highlight its use. Saeki says, "I felt that Tsurido was perfect for hardware advertising. That twitching sensation when a fish nibbles at the line is just right for the Dual Shock Controller."

Soon after the ad campaign started in late March of 1998, Tsurido sales jumped—from five thousand units in February to fifteen thousand in March and twenty-five thousand in April. Although it is uncertain to what extent this contributed to hardware sales, Saeki says, "We can call the campaign a success if one thousand of the sixty thousand consoles sold every week were sold as a result of the ads."

Saeki now had absolute confidence in his tactics. SCEI had spent on advertising only a small portion of the company's consolidated sales of $7 billion. In view of the success of the ad campaigns, Saeki considers this an outstanding achievement. "I'm constantly surprised how low the proportion of our advertising and promotion costs are compared with total sales. I'm convinced that this contributes a great deal to our profits. Our promotion capability has been strengthened significantly in the past three years. Our weapons are excellent interpersonal relations, planning capability, expertise, and knowledge. If we put our minds to it, we could sell anything, even sailing ships or aircraft."

To be sure, Saeki has had to learn from his mistakes. In the fall of 1995, a year after the PlayStation was launched, SCEI produced its own software title, Beyond the Beyond, as part of a policy of building a stronghold in RPG (role-playing game) software, then the most popular game genre. One day, when Saeki was mulling over possibilities for a year-end ad campaign, a member of the software-production team said to him: "This game is brilliant. It will definitely sell a million copies." The staffer's confidence persuaded Saeki that he had to make the game a hit product, and he began formulating plans on the spot.

In part because Saeki was not an avid RPG player, he did not bother checking out the game himself. Furthermore, he had such confidence in SCEI's marketing capabilities that he felt he could sell a million copies of *any* title.

Saeki fell back on his forte, teaser ads—which had been so successful during the PlayStation's debut—this time using unfamiliar symbols in a sophisticated slogan: "BeyoBeyo>RPG>Playstation." The campaign was instantly successful, and the title initially sold 400,000 copies. After that, however, sales trailed off, and Saeki began to hear negative feedback from core users: "That game is no good. It's a lousy game." Saeki then played the game himself for the first time, and realized it was boring.

Who was at fault? It is easy enough to blame the game producer, but their confidence in their own creation cannot be faulted. Saeki laments: "It was my fault for taking their words at face value. I'd been in advertising for ten years and should have known the rule that only good products are worth advertising." But he remained resolutely positive in his outlook. He was grateful that he learned the lesson early, in only the first year after the PlayStation's release. Needless to say, he vowed that he would never make the same mistake again.

Saeki's ad campaign had been fueled by a feeling of indignation over a news reporter's interview of Hiroshi Yamauchi, president of Nintendo. In June 1997, Saeki read another quote from Yamauchi, from a speech delivered at a company meeting, in the newspaper *Asahi* that made him think the game war had reached a watershed: "'Sony is dominating the market, and Nintendo has fallen behind in the race. When I go down to Akihabara, I get the impression that the Nintendo 64 is going to be obliterated.' This statement horrified game-industry analysts from domestic and foreign securities firms. Yamauchi had admitted that the PlayStation had overtaken the Nintendo 64 by a big margin. The 170 participants at the meeting could not conceal their amazement: They couldn't believe that Nintendo's president, always so emphatic that PlayStation users were just a handful of dedicated gamers, had calmly admitted that Sony has won!"

EXPANDING THE USER BASE: NEW ATTRACTIONS

One of the reasons the PlayStation had become so popular was SECI's deliberate attempt to expand the user base. An illustration of this effort is the PlayStation advertising campaign, which was carried out in two phases: Until sales of 2 million consoles was achieved in May 1995, the campaign was directed at core game users. Advertising focused on assuring users that the PlayStation format was firmly established by creating the impression that SCEI would continue to devise ways to please.

After the 2-million-unit milestone was reached, the target of advertising was extended to general consumers, a shift clearly reflected in content of the ads themselves, many of which contained images that were like scenes from a TV series and had little to do with the game being promoted. One ad, proclaiming "Golf Is for Everyone," showed a group of senior citizens sitting in front of a TV screen playing a golf game. An ad for Derby Stallion, a horse racing game, featured a high school student talking to herself on the way to school; the game's title was displayed for a only brief moment at the end of the commercial.

The 1997 year-end campaign "A PlayStation Is Your Reward" and the spring 1998 "Get a Charge Out of Life" campaigns also targeted the general public. By then domestic shipments of the game had surpassed 10 million consoles, and most users who were inclined to buy one had done so. The new target was the group of users who were resistant to advertising that emphasized novelty and functionality. Saeki explains, "It was a shift from advertising aimed at core users to making PlayStation a part of daily life. After we'd sold as many as ten million units, market segmentation was impossible, and it became difficult to target a particular segment of the market. We needed to change our approach and find common denominators among user groups. But what users have in common is their daily lives. So we focused on lifestyle. For example, young people without boyfriends or girlfriends have time on their hands. So how can they kill time? With the PlayStation, of course!" This was the thinking behind the slightly far-fetched but highly successful "PlayStation Is a Daily Necessity" campaign. Today, although 12 million units have been sold in Japan, tens of thousands more are sold every week.

SCEI continued its efforts to expand the user base in the area of software as well. The price of a PlayStation software title had originally been set at $58, or half that of Super Famicom software. Tokunaka says: "We wanted to expand the user base, and to make that happen we wanted the next generation of PlayStation users to enjoy popular titles of the past. We'd already recouped our investment in software production because of some hit titles, and this meant we could relaunch an existing title at a cheaper price. The greatest appeal to those who were thinking of buying a game machine was that we offered a PlayStation "Greatest Hits" library. We were sure that users would love it." The "Greatest Hits" titles were released for $28 each.

In selling discounted second- and third-issue copies of a work on which the publisher has recouped its investment, SCEI was merely following the conventions of the record industry, which reduced the price of record CDs from $38 to $28 when they were still new to the market, a move that proved to be quite popular. SCEI carried out many simulations to make sure that software producers and retailers still made a profit at the reduced price and royalties of these titles.

The change in the royalty structure that went into effect on April 1, 1998, illustrates the point. Until then, the OEM price per copy of a software title had been $9 across the board, making the retail price, which reflected the cost of software production, advertising, and profit, an invariable $58. SCEI wanted price flexibility, however, in order to increase the number of users in the future. "So we decided to link royalties to the retail price, making it easier for producers to issue software at various prices and packages that combined several disks," says Tokunaka.

The new royalty structure was based on the following formula: 15 percent of retail price plus manufacturing cost. For a standard $58 title, the royalty would be 15 percent of $58 plus the CD-ROM disk manufacturing cost (including the cost of a standard CD case), which came to $9, the same as before. For a title retailing at $38, however, the royalty would be $2 less, and software producers could maintain their margins. SCEI also offered a deal whereby producers had to pay the disk-manufacturing cost (without royalty) for the first CD in the package.

This royalty system made it easier for producers to issue multi-CD packages. SCEI applied the same terms to demo CDs: there was no royalty for any but the first CD in an album. The arrangement capitalized on the advantages of CD-ROM as a software medium, and would not have worked if SCEI had adopted mask ROM cartridges. These strategic adjustments to price the software price structure showed SCEI's great skill as a fast-growth platform developer.

SCEI knew that to expand its user base it also had to offer ever-greater variety in its software—that is, a selection of software that attracted not only core game users but people who had previously had no interest in games. Parappa the Rapper is one game SECI executives hoped would have this broad appeal.

Outside creators were recruited to develop the game: The executive producer was Masaya Matsuura, a Sony Records musician, and artist Rodney Greenblatt was responsible for visual design. The game features Parappa, the hero, who learns how to play rap and captures the heart of girlfriend Sunny Funny. A teacher praises the player who gets a good rap rhythm using the controller buttons, and becomes angry at a player who doesn't.

The game, which spawned a whole new game genre called "rhythm action," in which music takes center stage, was totally different from traditional RPGs and went beyond a simple action game. Its 2-D-style images further differentiated it from other PlayStation games, most of which featured 3-D images.

Parappa the Rapper went on sale in December 1996; it sold 300,000 copies by the end of the month, and 500,000 by the end of January. It has been bought by a broad spectrum of users, 40 percent of whom are women, compared with an average of 10 percent for other titles. SCEI successfully managed to expand PlayStation's user base.

5 CHAPTER

Making the Winning Game Machine: The Intelligence of Algorithms

MAKING THE MOST POWERFUL GAME MACHINE.

1994 was the heyday of multimedia. Everyone said that the only way for communication media to survive was through multimedia. Next-generation game machines were always a central theme of this topic. Because these machines were of extremely high specification, they were known as the "gateway to multimedia." They were defined not as children's toys, but as entertainment tools that adults, too, could enjoy.

Some manufacturers overtly described their products as "multimedia machines." For example, Matsushita Electric originally described its 3-DO as a multimedia machine, although the product was marketed as a game machine. Likewise, NEC gave its PC/FX long-term marketing as a multimedia PC. It was a common practice at the time.

PlayStation was totally different. From the start, Sony made it clear that the PlayStation was *not* a multimedia machine. Sony didn't claim the product was an all-around performer, but that it did one thing well. Teruhisa Tokunaka, Sony vice president at the time, emphasized: "This is not a multimedia player. It's a game machine. It doesn't play games as a part of multimedia; it only plays games." This was the essence of PlayStation.

This approach is easier to understand when compared with that of the 3-DO. According to a Matsushita press kit, "You can enjoy a wide range of software on the 3-DO, from games to hobbies and sports, education, publishing, movies, and more." Although Matsushita gave the impression that it was marketing the 3-DO as a comprehensive multimedia machine, in practice the emphasis was on game software. Perhaps because of this marketing confusion, sales of the 3-DO were lackluster. The company planned first-year shipments of one million units, but domestic shipments totaled just 200,000 units, and eventually the 3-DO was withdrawn from the market.

Viewed against this marketing approach, the Sony tack of attempting to win the trust of users and the industry by defining PlayStation as a game machine, not multimedia, was truly strategic. At the end of the day, users of this type of machine are game lovers, and machines that give them the games they want are the ones that sell.

From another perspective, game machines are high-performance computers. It is tempting to think that they could be sold as multimedia machines because of their tremendous information-processing capability, but Sony did not take that route with PlayStation. "How you define what you're doing is important," says Tokunaka. "We named our company Sony Computer Entertainment because we expected to grow only in that area. Games were the most important target because they were central to the business. So we refused to use the word 'multimedia.' We didn't like the vague impression it gave."

So the one area in which Playstation specializes was pushed to its limits by its creators and made as powerful as possible. There is no doubt that this was one of the major factors in PlayStation's success. What was the secret that made this possible?

THE BEAUTY OF ARCHITECTURE TRANSPLANTED FROM SYSTEM G

The starting point of PlayStation is System G, a 3-D computer graphics technology developed at the Sony Information Processing Research Institute, which astonished Kutaragi when he first saw it in 1984. PlayStation was System G applied to a game machine. The power of PlayStation is the power of System G.

What was so remarkable about System G? "At the time, System G was the only technology in the world capable of real-time texture mapping," said Akio Ohba, currently deputy manager of the architecture research department at SCEI's R&D Division, which developed System G. "Other companies' systems could do it if they took time to do the calculations, but none of them could do it in real time."

So why did such technology exist at Sony then? "We were able to do it, because we had a clearly defined objective," reflects Ohba. "Kutaragi recruited more than ten digital technologists from Sony"s various research institutes for the start-up of PlayStation, and Ohba was one of them. System G was developed for special effects in broadcasting equipment. It was a dedicated piece of equipment with a single purpose, not for general use. We didn't have to consider other requirements, so it was possible to enhance performance to the farthest limits."

The secret of the speed of System G was parallel processing by ten dedicated processors. Until then, parallel processing had been considered possible in theory, but there were no actual success stories. It was particularly difficult to make parallel processing work with graphics applications. Ohba, however, achieved real-time computer-generated graphics by using dedicated instead of general-purpose processors. Dedicated processors, customized for speed, allowed a texture-mapped image to move easily in real time.

From the start, the goal of using System G was precisely defined as the synthesis and modification of images on a TV screen. The System G development team and Sony's broadcasting equipment design team were on the same site and were in frequent contact, and the System G team had a good grasp of the other team's requirements. According to Kutaragi, "We made our task simple, without using any unnecessary resources. It was the beauty of an algorithm that fits its purpose perfectly."

However, there is another theory as to how the team managed to create a technology like System G. "It's because we were amateurs," argues Akira Okamoto, today manager of the Architecture Research Division of the SCEI Research and Development Headquarters, which developed System G with Ohba. "I'm an electrical engineer, and Ohba majored in biotechnology. We are both complete amateurs when it comes to software. We were able to design System G freely, without being restricted by the conventions of computing at the time. Even if others told us that we were trying to do the impossible, we kept going. Even I could build a computer that can do multiplication with 'and' and 'or' logic devices, counters, and four 4-bit arithmetic processors. We did everything ourselves."

Instead of using a ready-made system, the team built one from scratch. Since the team had a clear-cut purpose and their ideas were derived from theory, the end product was simple to produce and apply. That System G was a reality by 1985, not just as a theoretical design but as an application, is proof of the genius that went into the creation of System G.

PlayStation embodies not only System G's basic 3-D computer graphics technology, but also System G's development as an original technology. In designing the PlayStation and constructing its architecture (basic software structure), Kutaragi incorporated the technology of System G. "The basic concept that flows from System G to the PlayStation is the requirement for architecture to be simple and beautiful," Kutaragi explains. "Specifically, it has to be simple, not use gimmicks, and be intelligent."

Being simple means being adaptable. The more basic theory the architecture contains, the greater its potential for adapting to future applications. This was the inherent beauty of System G. "For example, you have to devise the architecture to facilitate future integration of semiconductors," Kutaragi explains. "It's no use making it based on the degree of integration at the time of design. Even if we buy LSI chips from several suppliers today, at some point in the future they will all be combined into one chip. When that day comes, the architecture must make it possible to combine them all." In short, it had to be architecture that allowed volume production and offered cost performance.

Second, Kutaragi's team knew it could not use gimmicks. It had to be sound technology that incorporated the principle of universality. "In other words," says Kutaragi, "we don't use clever, superficial techniques. It is possible to solve a problem using stopgap technology that works for the time being, but that would make it difficult to keep up with future technological advances." Again, the crux of the matter was whether the architecture could cope with future technological sophistication.

It is natural for game creators to strive for better expression, and it is the hardware manufacturer's task to produce machines that allow for more sophistication in games. The architecture must be able to cope with this requirement. Good architecture has depth and produces better results the more you work with it, surprising you with what it can do. "Moreover, the architecture must not be a product of chance, but must be deliberately conceived," says Kutaragi. "That's why the process we use to produce the architecture must be grounded in sound principles."

Kutaragi believed that he had to design the architecture himself, so he enlisted the help of Ohba and Oka, the developers of System G. Kutaragi had regularly visited various Sony research institutes to identify the elite who were likely to help him when his project got off the ground. He recruited Ohba and Oka when they were working on post–System G projects such as basic computer graphics research, animation production, and research in human interface.

Kutaragi put primary emphasis on real-time capabilities and response in PlayStation's hardware design. A game would not work if the screen did not respond immediately to input from the controller. To make this possible, a multitude of calculations must take place to synthesize the next image while one image is displayed on the screen. Processes such as matrix calculation to determine the polygon peak coordinates that move in response to input from the controller, image, and voice extension, rendering (applying the desired color to each polygon), and texture mapping (giving substance to screen images), all have to be completed in one-sixtieth of a second, the time it takes to compose one TV field. How could such a feat be achieved—and inexpensively—on a home-use game machine?

SHOOT FOR SPEED!

Before PlayStation, 3-D graphics arcade games used a pipeline processing type of architecture, which puts the CPU and DSP in a straight line and processes information like a conveyor belt. Graphics processing occurs as follows: First come the coordinate calculations; the results are passed on to the light source calculations; finally, these data are used for rendering calculations. Even the state-of-the-art graphics workstation sold at the time by Silicon Graphics for more than $100,000 had the same architecture.

SIGGRAPH, an entertainment-oriented academic conference for those interested in computer graphics, was held every summer in the United States, with researchers, artists, and equipment manufacturers from all over the world in attendance. Kutaragi attended SIGGRAPH several times to enjoy the atmosphere of leading-edge technical innovation. "Something didn't feel right, though," he says. "For example, virtual reality was very popular at one stage. You connect an expensive specialist graphics supercomputer to a head-mount display, which you slip over your head, and your field of vision enters a virtual world generated real-time by 3-D computer graphics. It was very exciting, because if you turned your head to the right, you would see an image on the right-hand side, and if you looked up, you would see the ceiling, and so on. But it felt rather weird; it made me feel as if I were drunk. I knew at once that the image didn't react immediately after I moved my head. The same goes for all commercial arcade games that used this technology."

For example, Virtua Fighter, an arcade game, used pipeline processing of ten rows of processors, 20 MIPS DSP each, to make a total of 200 MIPS. This is fast, but the movements are still strange. The game doesn't react immediately to input from the pad. The same goes for the arcade version of Ridge Racer, which has a small time lag between turning the steering wheel and screen movement. The reason for this lag lies in the actual movement of pipeline processing. In pipeline processing, the time needed to produce one field increases at each "handover" stage between rows. In ten-row pipeline processing, assuming a handover time of 16 milliseconds, the total time lag for the ten rows is 160 milliseconds. In other words, the screen will begin to move 160 milliseconds after inputting the command to move. This is inevitable in a processing structure that requires handovers.

Kutaragi decided to trade on his experience with System G and adopt a parallel processing architecture. The processing capacity of the R3000, a 32-bit RISC/CPU core developed by Mips Technologies, which he had decided to use as the CPU, was 30 MIPS, but he needed at least 800 MIPS to achieve the 3-D drawing performance required for PlayStation. He had to use parallel processing to reduce processing time. So, in the tradition of System G, he adopted the method of arranging numerous dedicated processors around the R3000 for parallel processing.

As a rule, many general-purpose processors are used when this kind of complex and fast calculation is required. For instance, the design of Sega Saturn was based on the architecture of previous 2-D arcade game machines. The dedicated processor and memory took care of generating the images and background. A separate processor and memory were responsible for the 2-D objects, with the two sets synthesized immediately before being displayed on the TV screen.

The Sega Saturn architecture was not originally intended for 3-D computer graphics. But when, halfway through the design phase, rumors were heard that PlayStation would specialize in 3-D computer graphics and Sega would have to compete against it, the Sega team was suddenly forced to work on 3-D coordinate calculations and light source calculations. The CPU that Sega had already decided to use lacked arithmetic capability, so the company decided to connect two of them in parallel. This, according to Kutaragi, was not beautiful architecture. He says, "Buildings that are made by adding several extensions may be adequate at the time, but will begin to fall apart over time, because they are not constructed properly. The Sega architecture will make it harder to combine LSIs in the future. In the first place, programming techniques for operating two CPUs efficiently are still at the research stage, and will prove to be an obstacle to game production, which has to be done in a limited time span." It is more "beautiful" to have a range of coprocessors linked by a simple, high-speed bus placed around a single general-purpose processor.

PlayStation inherited other techniques from System G, such as the simplification of calculations. Matrix calculations are simple and easy to process, so all tasks (such as light source operations, which express how light shines on surfaces; coordinate operations, which determine the location of 3-D objects; and perspective operations, which locate images projected on the screen) are first converted to matrix calculations before the calculation begins. As a result of adopting these various modifications, PlayStation achieved a processing capability of 1.5 million polygons per second. This would have been inconceivable a few years earlier, even with a dedicated graphics workstation.

So how was this "beautiful" algorithm developed and how was it reflected in an actual game? "We recently learned that PlayStation's capability was much greater than we imagined. It was a new discovery that if we use hardware cleverly, we can achieve significant results even with today's technology," says Kazunori Yamauchi, a game creator and former employee of SCEI's Production Division, who has now established his own company, Polyphony Digital.

Yamauchi is the developer of a major hit software product called Gran Turismo, a racing game. The game, which went on sale in December 1997, immediately went to the top of the charts and sold 4.6 million copies worldwide. Computer graphics illustrator Ryoji Kimura wrote about Gran Turismo in the April 25, 1998, issue of *Nihon Keizai Shimbun*, a daily national business newspaper: "Racing games are popular, and many of them are poorly crafted, but Gran Turismo is one that is well made down to the finest detail. . . . It's difficult, but you make steady progress if you work at it. The replay function that plays back your driving performance is delightful. The realistic effect of light reflected on the car body, which looks highly polished, is likely to be widely imitated in future racing games. The menu design with simple graphics throughout is also cleverly done. It's a game that brings a new element of aesthetics to racing games."

What Yamauchi means by "using hardware cleverly" is designing machines that show special effects, such as the light reflected on the highly polished car body in Gran Turismo, to their best advantage. Those who see this effect are amazed at how realistic computer graphics can be. Simple reflection has been seen before, but no other software product can match the way Gran Turismo reflects the very shape of the car body while depicting the surrounding landscape in a visually appealing way. How was this effect achieved? "It's a technique called environmental mapping," says Yamauchi. "When I first considered using it, I thought it was too difficult and that I should wait until the next-generation platform came along, but when I tried it on the current PlayStation, it worked."

When a new platform appears, its hardware capabilities are usually not fully utilized at once, because software creators must first get accustomed to it. As they gain experience with the new platform, creators begin to understand how to distribute data well.

The Performance Analyzer, created by the SCEI Development Department, is a convenient tool that shows creators in the form of charts and tables how their programs operate PlayStation's resources, to what extent they are using up PlayStation's capability as a platform, and whether there is any spare capacity. "Gran Turismo probably has the highest resource-utilization rating of all current software products, but there's still another 25 percent that can be developed," says Yamauchi.

This extra capacity is exactly what Kutaragi was aiming for: an architecture that allows creators to bring out the potential of hardware long after the launch. Says Managing Director Kitagami of Konami, "The definitive condition for successful hardware is the existence of software with unique, entertaining features that can only be enjoyed on that particular hardware. The crucial point about PlayStation as a medium is that it advanced from traditional 2-D to 3-D, and the primary reason the format became so successful is that a series of software came out that made use of the new method."

THE "SYSTEM ON SILICON" CONCEPT

The design of a game machine, however intelligent its architecture may be, does not end there. The algorithm must be incorporated into real circuitry—and at the lowest possible cost. All game machines before PlayStation, without exception, incorporated existing technology into the hardware in the form of a board. The design of all game machines consisted of a combination of general-purpose microcomputers and LSI chips. Kutaragi's thinking was radically different. "I decided to use customized semiconductors to perform the functions we wanted. The quickest response could not be achieved with existing LSI chips and parts. So instead of relying on what was available, I opted for the policy of building in all the functions we wanted on silicon." Although this approach to system LSI chips is common today, it was truly innovative in the early 1990s.

So how could the architecture be burned onto LSI chips? The important point here was the timing of development: It was essential to ascertain the timetable of advances in semiconductor technology and volume production. "The best strategy," says Kutaragi, "is to complete development immediately before semiconductor manufacturing infrastructure is in place and quickly get established using that infrastructure. The question is how quickly you can capture the market with a product using chips from state-of-the-art production facilities. If you get the order wrong, the result is disastrous. If you release the product too soon, you won't be able to produce enough volume and costs are high. You won't be able to replenish depleted stocks. On the other hand, if the timing of the release is too late, everyone catches on to the idea and you lose out to the competition."

Kutaragi thought carefully and concluded that PlayStation had to go on sale in the second half of 1994. In fact, he had started making timetable calculations when he first saw System G in the fall of 1984. He had joined forces with Nintendo, but he still believed Sony could go it alone when the partnership floundered, because he had absolute confidence in the timetable.

Others at SCEI had only a vague awareness of the significance of the launch date of December 3, 1994. Kutaragi, however, was convinced that the launch *had* to occur around this time. "It was the only possible timing if we were to complete product development before the infrastructure was completed. December 3, 1994: Every biorhythm was building toward a critical juncture on that date," says Kutaragi.

Kutaragi realized the importance of releasing the PlayStation at the point when the old industry format was giving way. He says, "The economy has its own rhythm and moves in a cycle with a specific frequency. You need to ascertain when the turning point will be." The 8-bit Family Computer ("Famicom") appeared in 1983. The 16-bit Super Famicom went on sale in 1990. There is a seven-year gap between the two dates. According to this pattern, the generation that followed the Super Famicom should appear in 1997, but because of acceleration of technology and other multiple factors, it was expected to emerge in 1994 or 1995. This timetable was widely accepted in the game industry.

Kutaragi based his release date on the evolution of semiconductor technology. But there were two variables in his prediction: He knew he had to obtain the LSI chips that control 3-D computer graphics based on System G. He also knew that the LSI chips had to be mass-produced. A prototype cannot be made into a business; the chip had to be ready for volume production. "A million units isn't enough. It must be ten times more, at least ten million units. I was convinced that PlayStation would sell on that scale," says Kutaragi.

What semiconductor could sustain a project of such scale? Who would make it? When could it be mass-produced? The answers to these questions held the key to successful entry into the game-machine market. The System G of 1985 used 20.000 ICs and LSI chips. How many years would it take to integrate these into a few LSI chips suitable for use in a home game machine?

THE SECRET TO AUTHENTIC SIMULATION

One of the principles Kutaragi followed was Moore's Law. Proposed by Intel cofounder Gordon E. Moore in 1965, it is an empirical law concerning the evolution of computer power, which is based on the evolution of semiconductor miniaturization technology. Moore's Law predicts that CPU processing capability will double every eighteen months.

Steady advances were being made in semiconductor miniaturization, and there was a strong possibility that every three years the width of lines in volume-produced semiconductors would be reduced by 30 percent, halving the required chip area. If, on the other hand, the area were kept constant, twice the number of transistors could be used, because transistors themselves roughly double their performance every three years. This means that, using the same architecture, the processing capability would be doubled. Based on these calculations, Moore's Law posits that processors will double their performance in eighteen months and quadruple it in three years.

Moore's Law applies to semiconductors that require upgrade compatibility, such as the microprocessors used in personal computers. However, in the area of 3-D computer graphics, which offers far greater freedom of architecture evolution, capability was improving at a rate of ten times every three years. Kutaragi identified the primary area of potential based on the speed of improvement of 3-D computer graphics. He thought that even greater progress could be achieved by changing the architecture itself, assuming that more transistors could be placed on a single silicon chip.

Taking everything into consideration, Kutaragi saw that for the system he envisioned there could be a potentially eightfold improvement in performance in three years. Moreover, he had learned from regular attendance at the ISSCC, an international academic society of semiconductor research, that the pace of semiconductor miniaturization technology was accelerating. Surely that meant a rate of improvement of ten times in three years.

How many of these tenfold improvements would be needed before System G, which comprises 20,000 transistors, could fit onto a single chip? To put 20,000 transistors on a chip, four cycles of advancement in the technology would be required, because $10,000 = 10^4$. Since one cycle takes three years, it would take $3 \times 4 = 12$ years for 10,000 transistors to be put onto a chip.

In 1985, the line width of LSI chips available for mass production was 1.4–2.0 microns (μ). Since the width of lines in semiconductors is reduced to 70 percent of the original width every three years, starting with a line width of 2.0 μ in 1985, it would become 1.4 μ in 1988, 1.0 μ in 1991, 0.7 μ in 1994, and 0.5 μ in 1997. It worked out that System G would fit onto two chips in 1997, twelve years after 1985. "As far as our calculations were concerned, our target was 1997, but taking into account the increasing pace of technical innovation, we thought ten years was probably a more accurate estimate of how long it would take," says Kutaragi.

This was the reasoning behind Kutaragi's timetable for the release of PlayStation—ten years or so after 1985, in 1994 at the earliest. "Half-micron process LSI chips were already completed in research centers in the late 1980s. There would be tens of thousands in the world in 1991. But that wouldn't be enough for volume production of game machines. Production in units of millions would become possible in 1994 or 1995."

The operating capability required for PlayStation was 800 MIPS, which meant one million gates. At the time, Sony's semiconductor division was capable of a maximum of 100,000 gates. Which semiconductor manufacturer was capable of designing a 0.5-μ-process, one-million-gate LSI chip, and would be able to begin volume production soon? Kutaragi, who had been gathering information from all over the world, chose U.S. manufacturer LSI Logic from his shortlist. Although LSI Logic is a well-known company today, it was a small concern in the mid-1980s and its management was far from stable. Nevertheless, Kutaragi was confident that this company could do what he wanted.

LSI Logic was reluctant to take on the task. Its main customers were manufacturers like Silicon Graphics (SGI), which produced workstations that sold for more than $100,000 per unit. Therefore, the LSI chips themselves were expensive items that saw frequent model changes.

LSI chips for game machines are totally different. Take the approach to model changes. Workstation LSI chips undergo a minor change every three months and a full model change once a year. Game machines, on the other hand, use the same LSI for several years. Game machines also require a much higher production. From LSI Logic's point of view, 100,000 units was a huge order, and an order of one million units was inconceivable. "They didn't think they could do what we asked," Kutaragi recalls.

Kutaragi persisted, because LSI Logic's ability to put system on silicon was outstanding. The company finally agreed, provided that Sony would bear the development cost. This proved to be the beginning of LSI Logic's success story; today, PlayStation LSI chips account for the bulk of the company's business.

Another problem to contend with was memory. Kutaragi says, "The other major factor that determines the specifications of a game machine is the performance and capacity of its memory. This is obviously dictated by the production capacity of semiconductor memory. If you are serious about the game-machine business, memory production capacity and the ability to source it are crucial. Once demand surges, the percentage of worldwide semiconductor memory production that can be devoted to the game machine becomes a key issue. You can't engage in this business unless you think that far ahead. If you work on the game-machine hardware without taking memory supply into consideration, you'll get stuck in no time."

It is no overstatement to say that game-machine sales were determined by the availability of semiconductor memory. Identifying the type of memory that could be mass-produced would effectively determine the product's specifications. Kutaragi was aiming for a product selling tens of millions of units, an unprecedented number for Sony products. He had to make detailed analyses of how much the price of the memory was likely to drop, and the estimated production capacity, investment status, and technological capability of the semiconductor company under consideration. "It's important not to use inappropriate memory, however good its performance," he says. "If, for example, it's the type of memory that goes from 1MB to 2 MB in the next generation, it would be very difficult to use. To make up 4 MB we would have to switch from using four 1 MB chips to two 2 MB chips, instead of one 4 MB chip. This would slow down data-transmission speed and fail to deliver the expected performance."

It was essential to identify what types of memory would become mainstream in the future. Game machines sell in large numbers, and a manufacturer's production can suffer if memory is in short supply, or is unusual and therefore difficult to find. The wrong forecast at this point could prove to be disastrous. So Kutaragi went directly to the suppliers for the answer. "I thought that Samsung Electronics of South Korea would soon become the world's number-one semiconductor manufacturer, because it had the technological capability, investment capital, and aggressive management to succeed," says Kutaragi. "So I met with Dr. D. J. Teng, then vice president of Samsung Electronics and the top manager of the semiconductor technical division, to ask him in detail about technical and worldwide trends in the industry. From the information I obtained, I became certain that EDO (hyper page mode) DRAM would become standard for PCs in the near future." EDO had the three essential attributes: It was amenable to performance improvements, it was easy to manufacture, and its cost was trending downward.

Kutaragi's homework paid off: EDO soon became the type of memory used more than any other in the industry. Needless to say, it is the memory used in the PlayStation.

THE REAL REASON FOR REDUCING PARTS COUNT

Kutaragi's predictions proved to be almost 100 percent accurate. The number of hardware parts used in the PlayStation fell with each successive model, although externally the product remained unchanged. The first PlayStation, released in December 1994 (SCPH-1000), had 750 parts. The fifth model (SCPH-7000), which went on sale in November 1997, had only 450 parts. Eventually, the number of parts used in the game was cut by almost half.

One day, Masatsuka Saeki of the public relations department wondered, "Why do we have so many engineers when we have only one item of hardware?" The answer can be found by disassembling the old and new PlayStations and comparing the contents. PlayStation had an architecture that allowed for research and engineering innovation— and, consequently, a reduction in the number of parts needed in each unit. This meant costs fell as production volume increased—a sure indicator of a successful product.

Generally, parts count is reduced to cut costs, but Kutaragi's thinking was unconventional. "It was to improve productivity rather than cut costs," he says. When PlayStation first went on sale, the production volume was 300,000 units per month, which was not a large figure for Sony. It was therefore possible to make the machines using the facilities of existing plants, with only a little additional investment. When monthly production rose to 700,000 units, however, the existing parts-packaging facilities could not deliver the required production capacity. The crucial machines at these facilities, called "chip placers," were very expensive items, and even if Sony decided to install additional units, it would take several months for the equipment itself to be made. And if sales of PlayStation took off, Sony would not be able to cope with the demand, especially when overseas markets were tapped.

Kutaragi ordered a long-term, systematic reduction in parts count to deal with this problem. The plan was implemented by Akira Tajiri, today a technical manager and managing director of SCEI. Tajiri knew that if you need a hundred different parts, even if they are inexpensive, you must have correspondingly diverse production facilities, which slows the rate of production. "If those hundred parts could be integrated into one, far fewer production facilities would be needed and the production process would be simplified, speeding up the rate of production significantly," says Tajiri.

Tajiri also focused on the printed circuit board (PCB). Here, too, the simple beauty of the original PlayStation architecture played an important role. Generally, when we talk about advances in PCBs, it means making multilayer boards, which enable packaging of a greater number of parts and ICs. Tajiri's idea, however, was to do the opposite: Simplify. He started with a double-sided, four-ply board. Then he used a double-sided, two-ply board, with parts packaged on both sides. He changed this to packaging on just one side, which dramatically improved productivity. Next, he reduced the size of the board, and today, at 12×19 centimeters, the board is two-thirds the size of the original one.

With any game-machine platform, hardware will continue to be made as long as the platform survives. So it is essential to build adaptability and cost-reduction potential into the hardware specifications. Kutaragi had the foresight to do this when he designed the PlayStation.

DESIGNER ON THE PRODUCTION FLOOR

Efficiency in volume production was pursued from the design standpoint as well. Teisuke Gotoh, art director at the Sony Corporate Design Center, was responsible for the design process. A unique aspect of his approach was that he specifically concentrated on "design that enables volume production."

Today's outstanding industrial designers consider not only form and raw materials, but productivity as well. Gotoh is a typical example. "Because volume production was a prerequisite, I made the design as simple as possible, with a form and composition that you could make with your eyes closed," he explains. He says that by simplifying construction he was aiming for a product that could be assembled on the production line in minutes.

Gotoh often visited the production floor, where he would discuss his design with engineers. Even when he was told that his design was not technically feasible, he did not abandon it. On the contrary, he would work together with engineers to find out what needed to be done to achieve his design concept in a way that improved overall productivity.

In the fall of 1994, not long before the first scheduled shipment of PlayStations, Sony's Kisarazu plant was in a mad rush to manufacture the game machine. It became evident that not enough controllers were being produced and that there would soon be a shortage. The main unit was being made at the rate of 300,000 units per month in December, and the production plan had called for the same number of controllers. Eventually Sony realized that it needed twice as many controllers, because competitive games are played by two people. Gotoh was horrified. There were not enough controllers, and there was no time to make more. It was obvious that they would end up with a shortage.

Another designer would have said that product shortages were not his problem, but not Gotoh. He went onto the production floor and stayed there until he discovered the problem. He learned that the process for pressing controller molds took one minute per item. If this could be reduced to fifty seconds, production would just about keep up with demand. Cutting the process to fifty seconds, however, resulted in a shiny surface that spoiled the appearance of the finished product. To prevent this, subtle adjustments of temperature and pressure of the metal mold were required. Gotoh spoke personally to the metal mold engineer and asked for his help. "They won't understand what we want if I just stay at my desk at headquarters and telephone them. If something's essential but it ruins the design, of course I must go down to the plant myself. You can't make a good product without doing this."

Another problem was that the black letters printed on the controller were not settling, making them difficult to read. The simplest way to solve this was to overprint, but this almost dou-bled the total time of the process. Gotoh asked one designer how they could solve the problem without increasing the time of the whole process, and together they discovered that if they put slight notches in the places where the words were printed, the ink would settle more deeply.

Gotoh stayed until he knew how dark the letters would come out, and until he was sure that the process would be car-ried out to his liking. This dedicated attention to detail resulted in PlayStation's magnificent design, quality, and ease of opera-tion. Moreover, his intervention did not result in a fall in pro-ductivity. Gotoh says, "In established areas like televisions, designers do not need to become so involved, because the sys-tem is already in place. But PlayStation was a first, so as a designer I had to be committed to that degree."

THE CLASH BETWEEN OHGA AND KUTARAGI

Kutaragi always gave top priority to ease of manufacture. This predilection led to what became known as the "caddy inci-dent," which was a clash between the principles of productivity and convenience.

Ohga ordered Kutaragi to put a caddy, a protective cover, on the disk. Ohga had a strong belief that optical disks, which expose the data side, must be protected in order to prevent acci-dents. He believed that a protective caddy was the best way to prevent problems such as children touching the disk with hands sticky with ice cream. Ohga's command led to putting a caddy on the CD-ROM Data Diskman and the MD. He also insisted that DVD disks should have caddies fitted.

"Fingerprints make replay difficult, and I was concerned that if children touched the disk's data side with their hands after eating ice cream or sweets, the signal couldn't be read and the customer service hotline would be inundated with unnecessary calls. So I suggested protecting the disk with a caddy," Ohga relates.

Kutaragi, however, adamantly opposed the president. "Mr. Ohga, we just can't do it. It will increase the media production cost, which will be reflected in the price. Worse, they will be harder to make and harder to use. I'm absolutely against it. Even though it's your command, I will not do it," he said, refusing to budge at all.

Sony wanted to reduce the price of PlayStation media to half that of Super Famicom media, which meant the CD-ROMs had to be low in cost and easy to mass-produce. Adding a caddy would increase the cost and the manufacturing time of the CD, making quick repeat production in response to market demand difficult. Furthermore, a caddy would make the CD harder to use and take up more space. Kutaragi's team insisted that the disadvantages of using the caddy far outweighed the advantages.

The relationship between Ohga and Kutaragi was similar to that between a stubborn father and a mischievous son. Both refused to compromise. They clashed head-on and argued loudly. Eventually, Ohga gave in. "Very well, I'll forget about the caddy. But you must make the PlayStation CD media different from other CD-ROM platforms and music CDs. If you just make silver CDs, they will all look the same." "Yes, sir," replied Kutaragi's team, and proceeded to come up with a black CD for the PlayStation. Ordinary CDs are shiny silver, with light reflected on the lacquered aluminum layer streaming through the clear polycarbonate board, but PlayStation disks are black from whatever angle you view them.

Ohga says, "Nintendo put cartridges on their mask ROMs that serve the same purpose as caddies, so not putting caddies on PlayStation CDs would make a stronger contrast. I argued with Kutaragi, but since caddies would delay repeat production, I conceded that Kutaragi was right on this point. Also, there were much fewer complaints about being unable to read the disk than I expected. CDs have been around for ten years, so I suppose parents have taught their children how to use CDs properly."

DRAWING SEGA INTO A PRICE WAR

After its launch, the PlayStation incorporated a number of potentially cost-cutting designs. As we've seen, parts count fell sharply, and there was a dramatic overall production cost reduction due to lower parts costs and fewer production processes. The greatest cost savings were realized not on the initial modest production volume, but on the much higher volume after sales of the unit started to soar.

The company took a substantial loss on the first model, which retailed for $399, but today the cost is a third of what it was then. The most strategic action in this respect was that sales revenues were not all plowed into profit, but were used in moves that would lower the retail price.

The retail price of the first model (SCPH-1000, launched in December 1994) was $399, the second model (SCPH-3000, released in July 1995) was $299, the third model (SCPH-3500, launched in March 1996) was $249, the fourth model (SCPH-5000, released in June 1996) was $199, and the fifth model (SCPH-7000, launched in November 1997) was $180. Needless to say, the fall in price led to expansion of the user base from die-hard game lovers to the general public.

There was another strategic purpose in slashing the price of the PlayStation: to draw Sega into a price war. In fact, Sony lowered the price in stages to make it easier for Sega to take up

the challenge. Kutaragi predicted that Sega would have difficulty reducing the high cost of the Saturn, because the Saturn
was a collection of parts supplied by different companies.

On November 22, 1994, the day the Saturn went on sale,
Gotoh immediately acquired one and took it apart. He was
astonished to discover how complex the structure was, with
cables running all over the PCBs. It was an inconceivable structure for Gotoh, whose design imperatives were simplicity and
ease of manufacture, and obviously much harder to manufacture than PlayStation's. If Sony reduced the price of PlayStation, Sega would have to follow suit in order to stay
competitive, but Saturn's high manufacturing cost would then
translate into huge losses for the company.

As expected, Sega took up Sony's challenge. When Sony
reduced the price of PlayStation by $100 in June 1995, Sega
began selling a set of Saturn hardware and software, with more
than $100 off the price of the two bought à la carte, and subse-
quently reduced the hardware price by $100 from $449 to $349.

By the end of 1995, Sega's counteroffensive had defeated
PlayStation. Although it was the year end, a time of peak
demand, PlayStation did not have many best-selling software
products. Sony found that PlayStation was outclassed by Saturn. "We were unprepared," Gotoh admits.

But Sony fought back. Sega could not help but retaliate
against Sony's attempts to provoke a price war. In February
1998, Sega changed its policy and decided to no longer pursue
volume by lowering the price of the Saturn. It was effectively a
declaration of defeat in the battle against PlayStation. In the fiscal year ended March 1998, Sega wrote off the cumulative
losses of its U.S. subsidiary and posted a loss of $4.3 billion,
going into the red for the first time since going public in 1988.

Sega published a full-page advertisement in the major
morning papers on May 21, 1998. The ad depicted a battlefield

from Japan's Country at War Era—the fifteenth and sixteenth centuries—with bodies of brutally slain armored samurai everywhere. The ad contained the Sega logo and a tattered flag. The copy read, "Has Sega been defeated for good?" The next day's papers carried another full-page ad, with exhausted warriors struggling to their feet. Sega was down but not out. Executives were regrouping to fight another day.

GOTOH: THE DISCRIMINATING SUPER-DESIGNER

Console design goes a long way toward making a winning game machine. The third person involved in the PlayStation project, in addition to technologist Kutaragi and marketing man Sato, was Gotoh, the designer. With his uncompromising spirit and attention to detail, Gotoh, like the other two men, overcame numerous obstacles and accomplished his goals, helping to create a new order in the world of computer games. "One of the main factors that led to the success of PlayStation," says Ohga, "was the design of the main unit and controller. We had various designs, but the one I adopted was totally different from the image of previous game machines in terms of quality and form."

PlayStation is the largest-selling single model the electronic equipment market has ever seen. No other game platform has sold 40 million units worldwide without a model change, and the PlayStation is expected to sell many more. (In audiovisual equipment, by comparison, a product that sells one million units is considered highly successful; if it is a new product, the manufacturer will declare the birth of a new genre. Moreover, Sony sold that 40 million PlayStations in just three and a half years after the game was launched, a truly remarkable achievement.) There is no doubt that one of the key factors in the amazing popularity of PlayStation is its sophisticated, timeless design.

"I'm convinced that the design contributed to the runaway success of the PlayStation," says Gotoh. "We had to start the PlayStation business with no track record. A major issue was whether software companies would publish titles for it. I thought the first hurdle was to ensure that game creators would like the hardware design. After all, game creators are the machine's first users. We've got it right if they think they want a platform that looks like ours."

For Gotoh, design is the very expression of content. The PlayStation contains only PCBs, a power source, and a CD-ROM mechanism. So first Gotoh thought about how he would reflect the content in a simple way. People easily tire of trendy round or square designs. Once fashion changes, that's the end of the product. If it is to survive, a design has to have a form that comes essentially from within. He thought of a soap package. The shape of a soap package is exactly the same as the shape of the soap itself. What could be more simple? Here, too, was the thinking behind System G: Simple is beautiful.

Gotoh was originally a designer of television sets. He was responsible for the Sony Profile PRO, a product that was well known for its sophisticated design and excellent performance. It was a distinctive product that became popular among audio-visual equipment buffs and was often found in the studios of TV stations.

Later, Gotoh was responsible for the so-called Sony miracle, the VAIO PC, a radically different computer that used magnesium materials and incorporated distinctive colors and shapes. It's no exaggeration to say that Gotoh's work embodies contemporary "Sony design."

This only underscores the excellence of the PlayStation's design. "TVs have a fixed shape and use the same devices. Within those constraints, I struggled to find ways to create innovative designs that are different from other products, how to emphasize the difference. But the game machine was completely different from conventional products, because the PlayStation is a one-and-only product. Although it competes against other platforms in the game-machine market, there are no other PlayStations."

Gotoh's approach was a pursuit of an eternal "one and only." What design would require no minor changes partway through its life? Gotoh had to find the answer. "Companies sometimes make minor changes to a product and change its shape, but in my view, that's because there's a fundamental problem with the design in the first place. I don't want to do anything like that. The time to change a product should be when you change what's inside. But there should be no need to change the exterior if you aren't changing what's inside," Gotoh insists.

For the PlayStation assignment, Gotoh began sketching on a blank piece of paper, first having rid himself of any preconceptions and opinions about existing game machines. What shape would it have? he wondered. What about the shape of the switch and the disk tray? He made dozens of sketches. The main theme he wanted his design to reflect was the CD-ROM format. He decided to model the game's primary shape on the CD-ROM idea. So he combined a square and a circle: He gave the machine a linear, square body and a round disk lid.

Game machines are sometimes carried in the hand. And the shape that best fits the human hand is a curve. So Gotoh made the top corners of the main unit right-angled, and he used arc corners on the base. This made the unit easier to carry in both hands; it felt snug when held in the hands.

Gotoh was uncompromising when it came to the user interface. He made the power switch large and round. This switch would be easily recognizable, with no sharp corners to cause injury, and the machine would be easy to switch on and off from any direction, even from behind. Since the machine would be used by children, Gotoh took special care to make the lid sturdy by making parts of it thick.

Gotoh designed not only the main parts of the PlayStation but also its peripherals, such as the memory card and later components, including the analog controllers. The distinguishing aspect of PlayStation design is the fact that Gotoh did it all himself. "Other Sony product categories have their own history and fixed design process, but there were no examples to follow with PlayStation, only a concept of doing something different from other products in the same genre," Gotoh says. "So I decided to take care of all products and peripherals for the game machine product category myself. Although I couldn't do that with products in conventional genres, I resolved to work on it until I was truly satisfied, because it was a genre we were tackling for the first time."

Kutaragi immediately approved of Gotoh's design of the main unit. He saw it as a design that expressed the essence of the whole PlayStation concept. "Although it did take time, ultimately, the first motif that came into my mind remained until the very end," says Gotoh. "The important question is how to allow pure concepts to take shape,"

"THERE HAS NEVER BEFORE BEEN SUCH A DIFFICULT PRODUCT"

Progress had been straightforward up to this point, but now the project hit an obstacle. When Gotoh showed Kutaragi the controller he had worked so hard to design, Kutaragi immediately rejected it: "What's this? The shape is original, but it doesn't look very easy to use." Most conventional controllers had the same basic shape developed for the Famicom controller: They were flat, were held in both hands, and the buttons were pressed by the thumbs. Gotoh's controller was nothing like it; if the conventional design can be described as planar, his was three-dimensional.

Gotoh first took his controller to Ohga. The Sony president usually criticizes prototypes, but he immediately approved of Gotoh's controller: "It's rather good. Very Sony." But Ohga was the only one who responded in this way. Others rejected it because it was so extraordinary, such a radical departure from conventional controllers. Kutaragi was one of its most vehement opponents. Kutaragi's team agreed that although the PlayStation was Sony's first product in the game-machine market, incorporating innovative technology and data-processing methods, the user interface should have the assets of established game machines—the button-operated controllers to which children were accustomed.

Pressured to change his design, Gotoh refused. It had taken him more than a year to produce his prototype. He was convinced that a machine spearheading a new generation of games should adopt a new controller shape. He recalls, "I have worked at Sony for twenty-one years now, but there has never before been such a difficult product. The controller was considerably harder to design than the console."

Gotoh carved a lump of acrylic foam and gripped it repeatedly to see how it felt in his hand; the shape of the controller was refined through countless repetitions of this process. Conventional flat controllers have to be held tightly during use, because the palm of the hand is not in contact with the grip; this tends to cause stress. Moreover, people have different-size hands, and distance between the hand and the buttons varies. If the distance is short, the grip must be even tighter.

Gotoh's thinking was completely different. His focus was how the controller could be held as naturally as possible. He considered a three-dimensional structure with a forward protrusion, like a grip, that could be held securely without clutching it tightly. "In fact, you don't grip it at all. You just support it from underneath with your fingers. Moreover, because there's a gap between the controller body and the fingers, even when you're engrossed in a game, perspiration doesn't accumulate. It evaporates away."

There came a time when Gotoh realized the advantages of a controller that does not make the user hold it in a certain way. He had assembled a group of children to test the controller. The children used the flat Super Famicom controller on a daily basis, so at first they were a little uneasy with the PlayStation controller, with its two solid grips protruding like horns, but they soon got used to it. Gotoh observed that once they learned how to use it, it did not seem to bother them at all that it had a shape different from that of other controllers. On the contrary, he received feedback that it was easy to use. He was encouraged, because children are honest: If they like something, they approve; if they don't, they say it's no good.

As he watched the children, Gotoh noticed that they were using the controller in ways he had not even imagined. They lifted it up and down, slanted it, controlled it from behind, wielded it in any way they liked. This was not possible with a flat controller, which had to be used in a fixed position, held in a particular way, and operated by a set finger movement. That it could be used in so many different ways told Gotoh that his design was full of potential. It was a true revelation for the designer.

OHGA: "THIS IS THE PRESIDENT'S COMMAND!"

However, Kutaragi, not to mention game creators at software developers, were still opposed to Gotoh's controller. Everyone wondered what was going to happen to the controller that

Gotoh had worked so hard to develop. The stalemate was resolved by a thundering command from Ohga: "As far as I can see, this grip-style controller is very easy to use, something that children and adults alike would enjoy using. Stop arguing and adopt this design!" He even went on to declare: "I'm the president, so you must do as I say. Otherwise, you're all fired!"

The design was finally accepted.

As he listened to Ohga, Gotoh felt that at last all his effort was being rewarded. He says, " I was really pleased that Chairman Ohga appreciated my design so much that he said what he did." Gotoh was reminded that Sony had a culture that respected the views of designers.

Ohga has his own reminiscences about the controller episode: "Kutaragi won the argument about the caddy, but my view prevailed regarding the controller. Some time later, I read an article in a computer game magazine that claimed that the secret of the PlayStation's success lay in the controller, which is gripped in both hands. I laughed heartily and said to Kutaragi, 'Look, I was right. It says so in here.' He replied coolly, 'Yes, Mr. Ohga, I was wrong about that, but I was right about everything else.' That's the really great thing about that guy."

6

CHAPTER

Sony's Love-Hate Relationships

To Sony, SCEI is an organization strategically founded to enter the game market. What, then, is Sony to SCEI, a company in which Sony and Sony Music each hold a 50 percent stake? And why did Sony decide to establish SCEI?

Says Ohga: "As the CEO, I wanted to be their biggest supporter." However, it was impossible for Ohga to devote himself to this one business night and day. "I had Iba look after the detailed management." Ohga was referring to Sony's chief financial officer and vice president, Tamotsu Iba, a managing director of Sony at the time. "In those days, Iba and Kutaragi frequently locked horns during disputes and Kutaragi would appeal directly to me."

Iba, who was responsible for day-to-day operations then, says: "Mr. Ohga frequently states that the PlayStation is a successful example of a venture business, but I don't think so. In the end, it was a Sony business. My view is that the situation is different than with other venture businesses in the sense that Sony personnel, capital, and manufacturing facilities were fully exploited."

In the summer of 1992, Iba returned to Sony after an assignment with Sony Life, a life insurance subsidiary of Sony, and assumed responsibility for the management strategy department. One of his responsibilities was consideration of new business opportunities. Kutaragi was a frequent visitor. "He was always walking around promoting seemingly preposterous visions. I never even imagined that the PlayStation would become the product it is. To be honest, my view was that the success or failure of this business would become known only after the fact. I was resigned to abandoning the business if worse came to worst."

For all of that, Kutaragi's words were persuasive enough to convince others to assume the risks involved. Iba continues: "Call it inspiration. A unique, one-of-a-kind inspiration.

What's the expression? Vision. That's it. But not only vision. He had the persuasiveness to convince people that it might just be achievable. That's why I thought, "If this guy says so, I'll certainly back him.' He was very cocky and self-assertive. You don't find many guys that self-confident in Sony. His strength lies in his ability to set goals. He announces extraordinarily ambitious objectives, but never off the cuff: They are underpinned by extensive study. He has studied and progressed further each time you meet him. He establishes ambitious goals based on accurate predictions of the state of development of semiconductor processes and the rules of architecture. That's why he's persuasive."

The period from 1992 to 1994 was a difficult one for Sony, with the company posting operating losses. Sony curtailed investment and reduced business activity throughout the group, and the mood in the company was gloomy. However, Iba's policy was to give Kutaragi and his team free rein. Iba recalls, "I thought that something promising and enjoyable was necessary at such a time more than ever."

Iba was recommending a joint venture, but the idea of Sony entering the game business on its own also arose. Says Iba: "Hardware and software are inseparable in the game business. I thought the two should be linked." On that premise, Iba proposed a joint venture to Sony Music, but Maruyama unexpectedly turned him down. From Iba's position, Maruyama, as head of Epic Sony game production, ranked as Kutaragi's boss. For this reason, Iba had anticipated that Maruyama would readily agree to a plan to establish a joint venture company.

Maruyama's refusal was prompted by the situation at Sony Music. Maruyama told Iba: "This business is extraordinarily risky for Sony Music. We would like Sony itself to assume as much leadership as possible, with our role limited to involvement in software production."

The relationship between Sony and Sony Music is not as monolithic as is generally thought. Sony views Sony Music as one subsidiary company, but Sony Music takes pride in having reached its current position without relying on Sony's assistance. Therefore, the subsidiary does not feel it must unquestionably obey the parent company. Maruyama's assumption was that Sony Music involvement would be limited to the domain of software. He desired a structure in which the main thrust of the game business, including platform management, remained with the parent company.

Iba, not yielding an inch, said: "The business structure is different for records and games. With records there is a de facto standard and an open format. That's why hardware and software can be successfully developed separately. But, because each game platform involves a closed format, separate development isn't natural. That's why we should do it jointly." Iba explains his reasoning: "Both Sony and Sony Music are listed companies. If Sony Music were to participate, it wouldn't be possible to run the business within Sony. A joint venture was the only answer. Besides, Kutaragi always used to say that the bureaucratism within Sony would hinder development of the business."

For his part, Maruyama responds to Iba's comments as follows: "That kind of rhetoric is characteristic of Mr. Iba. Matsushita suffered no sustained damage from the failure of 3-DO. But from the standpoint of Sony Music at the time, there could be no such thing as a superficial wound. And so the truth is that as far as possible we wanted to reject the idea. If it had been proposed by a third party, we would certainly have refused."

Nevertheless, Iba eventually succeeded in bringing about the joint venture, forcing Sony Music's participation. Maruyama comments: "That's what came about in the end. I never in my wildest dreams thought we would be involved to this extent. You see, the risk was so great."

Maruyama was not the only person at Sony Music with concerns. The Sony Music corporate planning office held the view that involvement in the game business would result in squandering money, and they were concerned that the entire premium realized when the company went public would be spent. However, with the decision to form the joint venture a reality, Sony Music could not ignore the situation. Having shouldered the risk, there was no possibility of withdrawal. Maruyama says, "Having reached that point, there was no option but to put our every effort into the business." The arrangement did not permit participation on a limited scale, but necessitated involvement in every aspect of the business.

Ohga says: "The fifty-fifty capital structure was another reason for the success. The equal capital split was a statement that hardware and software carried equal importance. You might well ask whether a company with a fifty-fifty share-capital arrangement is difficult to manage because of differences of opinion, but I was ultimately responsible for both companies. So my word was final. That issue was easily settled."

CASH FLOW MANAGEMENT

Although it was a difficult climate for investment, in keeping with the share-capital ratio Iba agreed to support half the financial requirements of the venture and gave the go-ahead to spend the required amount without restriction. However, he did not neglect to place a condition on his former subordinate Tokunaka: "In return, you must always be sure to maintain a positive cash flow." Iba had a strong conviction: "The issue isn't whether profitability is a matter of opinion. It's that cash is reality."

Modern financial accounting is a system that examines the activities of companies during a specified period of time. When Iba says, "Profitability is a matter of opinion," he expresses the view that profitability or lack of profitability is determined by accounting decisions. In other words, profitability is arbitrary, and a company's situation cannot be accurately determined only from a profit-and-loss statement. That's why "cash is reality"; a company's situation can be accurately interpreted from its cash-flow position.

In the United States, cash flow is managed as a matter of course, and share price evaluation is based on cash flow. Borrowing from this practice, Sony has adopted cash flow, in addition to profit and loss, as an important management indicator for the parent company, each group company, and all operations included in the consolidated financial statements. As Iba recalls: "This was devised during the painful period at Sony from 1992 to 1994. It goes without saying that, in addition to profitability, cash flow including cost depreciation is an important performance index for new companies as well."

Watching cash flow is only part of it. In fact, management approach differs according to whether the cash-flow position is positive (there is cash on hand) or negative (the company must borrow funds). A start-up company incurs early losses as a matter of course, but provided it is successful, the losses are soon recouped and profits earned. The cash-flow position turns from negative to positive.

Of course, SCEI was no exception. Cash-flow management is all about leading the company to a positive cash position, devising ways to generate additional cash, and using that cash as effectively as possible. Iba said to Tokunaka, "The ways to improve cash flow are to reduce inventory, quickly convert it into cash, and collect receivables." Acting on Iba's instructions, the area upon which Tokunaka focused was credit policy—that is, payment and collection terms. Tokunaka points out: "As a rule, cash shortages arise because capital requirements increase with growth, and I paid a great deal of attention to structuring credit policy for payables and receivables. Contrary to the norm, I structured things so that cash flow improved with growth."

The specifics involved careful attention to debt collection. The conventional notion in the industry until that time was that game software sold through wholesale distributors was priced by the lot, and that generous credit terms were necessary to compensate distributors for inventory risk. However, the PlayStation is a game platform designed in pursuit of maximizing stock turnover. This was the trump card that contributed to preserving positive cash flow. That is, by taking advantage of the nature of CD-ROM titles, which permit fast fulfillment of replenishment stock, SCEI reduced risk and eliminated the necessity of extending long credit terms.

Formerly, industry practice was to close distributor accounts at the end of the month and collect the proceeds from the month's sales at the end of the following month, but SCEI instituted a short-term credit policy involving closing accounts on the twenty-fifth and collection on the tenth of the following month. This reduced the receivables term by half compared to the established practice. At the same time, by arranging for payment terms to be longer than collection terms, SCEI structured cash flow so that cash on hand would accumulate. Says Tokunaka: "Debt collection is a question of our motivation. It involves constant resolve to collect. Because we shortened the customary payment term, we received frequent complaints from resellers. But we devoted ourselves to obtaining their understanding and collecting the amount due. We paid careful attention to the importance of cash flow in managing the business."

A July 20, 1993, business plan review meeting attended by Ohga, during which Tokunaka submitted a business simulation plan, drove the point home. At the meeting Tokunaka said, "We request access to a maximum of $90 million in seed capital," and the basics of the plan were approved. Tokunaga's careful attention to cash flow stemmed from this meeting.

The result was miraculous. The PlayStation business was launched at the end of 1994, and in Tokunaka's words, on a monthly basis "we were somehow able to maintain a positive cash flow position at all times." As for the actual seed capital requirement, "It was touch and go, but somehow we were able to stay within the $90 million limit agreed upon with Mr. Ohga." Positive cash flow was achieved despite initial cumulative losses because Iba and Tokunaka's views coincided.

Sony's financial results for fiscal 1997 show that SCEI had made great strides, with the PlayStation accounting for 22 percent of Sony's consolidated operating profit. Iba's praise is effusive: "No other individual business unit in the Sony group generates profits on such a huge scale. It is an enormous contribution to Sony. It's an unprecedented success, even for Sony. In the end, spinning it off as a separate company proved to be the key to success."

As we have seen, SCEI grew rapidly, carefully nurtured by Sony. However, all was not warmth and tender support. There was discord which necessitated that SCEI outgrow the existing relationship.

THE UNEXPECTED PRICE-REDUCTION ANNOUNCEMENT: THE DISPUTE WITH SONY

May 1, 1995. Los Angeles.

The Electronic Entertainment Expo (E3), a specialty game trade show, was thrown into tumult by an announcement from SCEI. In addition to announcing that the U.S. version of the PlayStation would sell for $299 (a price position $100 lower than the previously announced price of the Sega Saturn), SCEI announced that it would launch a revamped Japanese model priced at $299, representing a $100 reduction in price.

It was not only the E3 exhibition site that was tumultuous. A tremendous uproar was also occurring at Sony headquarters. The reaction "What on earth are they thinking?!" reverberated throughout Sony in response to the price reduction. Why was Sony in such a state of agitation?

May 29, 1995. Twenty-eight days after E3. A hotel in Tokyo.

In attendance at a gathering held to commemorate PlayStation shipments surpassing one million consoles, Tokunaka remarked in a speech: "To further expand the business, we introduced a low-priced model. The next objective is three million units in the first year."

Hearing this, reporters from the daily newspapers became animated. They had not heard of the announcement at E3. The following day's newspapers not only made note of the whopping $150 price difference compared to Sega Saturn, they also reported that the business was in top form: "PlayStation sales are strong, with a total of one million units shipped from the launch in December of last year through the fourth week in May" (May 30, 1995, edition of the *Nihon Kogyo Shimbun* newspaper).

However, the reality was completely different. By that time the PlayStation was no longer in top form. To be sure, the business *had* been in top form until March of 1995. Inventories were in short supply at retail stores and product shortages had become chronic. But as March arrived, the PlayStation stopped selling without warning. Once sales reached the 600,000–700,000-unit level, momentum suddenly dissipated.

SCEI launched Tekken in March, but sales did not develop as anticipated. Developed by Namco, Namco's Tekken was highly popular at arcades, and everyone said it couldn't fail to be a major hit if modified for home use. As good as the software was, it didn't sell as well as SCEI expected. Tokunaka analyzes the situation: "We figured it out right away. The user group that will spend $399 on game hardware —the core user segment— were already familiar with Tekken. The Tekken introduction didn't stimulate sales and we faced a serious problem."

There was still another strange development. The actual selling price of the PlayStation had not yet fallen. The game machine continued to sell at list price long after launch, even at discount stores. The PlayStation's popularity and product shortages contributed to keeping the market price at the $399 list. Moreover, although SCEI had inadvertently offered a trade discount 10 to 15 percent more favorable than that of the other game manufacturers, this had not contributed to reduced selling prices.

"Cut the price!" The idea just came up. Take the bull by the horns and reduce the price. There's room for a cut of, say…$100. Kutaragi says: "The fact is that it had been our intention to start lowering the price when the timing seemed right. The business structure and margin structure of the game business is different from that of Sony's audiovisual products. You must earn a reasonable profit on sales of AV equipment, but with game machines you draw up a combined profit portfolio for hardware and software. Even if you have to reduce the price of hardware, you profit from the software sales that increased console sales bring. It's commonplace. If anything, continuous price reductions over time is the proper state of affairs."

The awareness that the actual situation didn't conform to this theory, the enthusiasm for the idea, and the desire to break out of the sales slump combined to leave only one conclusion: "Cut the price! By $100!" With that, SCEI suddenly announced the price decrease from $399 to $299 at E3. They simultaneously announced to resellers a reduction in the trade discount.

But opposition was heard from an unexpected place. It came from Sony's domestic sales headquarters. There was strong criticism that lowering the list price and cutting trade discounts less than six months after launch flew in the face of accepted business practices in the audiovisual industry and was wholly without precedent. Some high-volume resellers were lodging complaints: "If you lower the price as much as $100, we will discontinue sales of Sony products." This reaction arose because the reseller margins on the PlayStation had been exceptionally high. Even Ohga expressed opposition: "Lowering the price of a Sony product without accompanying product modifications is out of the question. There has never been an instance in the history of the company of reducing the price of a product once it's on sale. There is no way to justify it to stores selling the current product, not to mention users who have bought it."

The reason relations had soured with Sony Corporation is that there had been no prior consultation on the issue. When taking such a major decision, it is customary to notify all concerned parties, provide information on all the particulars, and seek consent well in advance; but this had not once occurred to Tokunaka, Kutaragi, or Maruyama. Their thoughts were occupied with nothing but clearing the next hurdle and returning the PlayStation to the path to growth. No one had even considered consensus-building at Sony headquarters.

The thoroughly enraged head of Sony's domestic sales headquarters, his countenance fierce, stormed into SCEI to complain. Tokunaga's response that "price reductions are totally natural with game machines" only added fuel to the fire and sent the Sony sales headquarters into a furious uproar. The SCEI team was grilled about the decision: "When you decided to lower the price, did you conduct careful simulations to determine the effect on the business? And based on the results, did you implement adequate countermeasures?"

The response of "No. We haven't done anything" raised concerns within Sony about whether the business was in capable hands and engendered talk that Tokunaka should be removed from management responsibility. A storm raged through Sony, and calls for Tokunaga's demotion or dismissal were heard repeatedly.

THE BOLDNESS TO SELL AT A LOSS

It was true that they hadn't conducted any simulations. Conducting or not conducting simulations would do nothing to change the certainty that the business would lose money. Because it was wholly uncertain when the losses could be reversed, simulations were of secondary importance. From the very beginning, the view at Sony had been that the business would be too small in scale to pay and would lose money. That's why the truth is that no one had even the motivation to conduct simulations.

February 1994 (ten months before launch).

The key members of SCEI lodged a night and two days at the resort hotel Mahoroba, located on the Miura Peninsula. The site had been converted into a hotel from a luxury condominium complex—built during the economic bubble—that had failed to sell. Brainstorming started at 7:00 P.M. in a suite with three bedrooms, a living and dining room, and a kitchen. It was an important meeting during which distribution policy and marketing methods were decided. The sole issue that couldn't be decided was the price of hardware. The youthful participants argued vociferously over the price, but because Tokunaka, Maruyama, and Kutaragi were absent, no decision was reached.

Tokunaka and Maruyama arrived at the Mahoroba well after 10:00 P.M. The discussions had finished and a party was in progress. Just as Tokunaka slid open the door to the banquet room a twenty-five-year-old up-and-coming woman from the sales promotion staff bounded over, threw her arms around him in a drunken embrace, and chanted "It's—gotta—be—$299!"

While locked in the stifling embrace, Tokunaka thought of the fine mess they had gotten into. The price of memory wasn't decreasing as they had forecast. Based on previous history, it was time for the price to start to drop, but against all odds the market price was rising instead. Prices remained unusually high owing to the aftereffects of booming personal computer sales. They recalculated costs only to find they rose each time. Because they were suppressing this information (they had not informed the employees), Tokunaka could only respond to the woman's shrill demand with a troubled countenance. Because the young woman was unaware of the situation, she was simply making the sound argument that lowering the price would increase market penetration, but...

"Two hundred ninety-nine dollars—no way—no way!" chanted Tokunaka in response. He repressed the temptation to voice his true feelings, enduring insistent demands concerning price from every corner of the room until the party broke up.

Kutaragi's theory was that the price of memory was certain to decrease with time, but his forecast was wide of the mark and the steep price increases continued. When the list price of $399 was set, the assumption was that memory prices would drop in the near future, but that assumption had proved completely false.

Nevertheless, despite the prevailing market circumstances, Kutaragi held to the optimistic view that memory prices were certain to fall: "This is nothing to worry about at all. If the peak is high, the valley is certain to be low. Besides, our competitors also use memory and face the same circumstances. That's why the real issue is how to minimize the damage."

In fact, the high prices continued for some time after that, and even at the time of launch toward the end of 1994 they were showing no signs of dropping. In fact, the high prices continued until the end of 1995. Nevertheless, forging ahead at a time when hardware sales would bring a loss was a highly successful strategy for the game-machine business. Matsushita Electric and Sanyo Electric with 3-DO, NEC Home Electronics with its proprietary PC-FX technology, Japan Victor's Sega Saturn–compatible "V-Saturn," and Hitachi's similar "Hi-Saturn" were all launched as efforts by electrical appliance manufacturers to enter the game machine market, and all ended in failure. Only SCEI was able to survive this period. What made the PlayStation different?

The decisive difference was that whereas the household appliance group followed an unmodified appliance business model, SCEI held true to the methodology of the game business. The appliance manufacturers used cost-based pricing and insisted on profitable hardware sales. By contrast, Kutaragi at SCEI preached: "Cost-based pricing will bring certain failure. Even if we sell below cost, it's still early in the program. Selling below cost at a time of high sales volume would be a major problem, but at this stage even if a loss is incurred, the total amount isn't very significant. More important, there is no future in the game market for cost-based pricing."

Kutaragi's model was correct: A game business should be structured so that the hardware is distributed free of charge and profits are derived from software sales. Nevertheless, while the model is intellectually simple to understand, the reality is unsettling when losses accumulate before one's eyes. Kutaragi continually preached the message: "Memory prices are certain to fall in the medium to long-term. From the broad prospective, this is bound to happen." Kutaragi was confident: "Hesitation now would be disastrous. We've been pursuing our dream. We should act more decisively."

Kutaragi's conviction quickly spread and the price-reduction proposal was approved in no time. The problem was that the question of how to handle Sony had not been addressed. Somehow a compromise had to be reached. On the verge of a stalemate, Kutaragi made a proposal: "If lowering the price of the existing model is unacceptable, why not change models? If the price is going to decrease, why don't we reduce performance?" This prompted the decision to remove the S Terminal. It was nothing more than a makeshift solution, but it was the only way to secure Sony's agreement. With that, they acted as though there had been a model change and won Sony's forgiveness.

What was the result of the price reduction? No sooner was the low-priced model "SCPH/3500" launched at a list price of $299 than it began to sell at an incredible pace. The momentum of sales far exceeded the pre-March level. According to theory, the effect of price elasticity is the square of the ratio of the new price over the old price, and in this case PlayStation sales proved the theory. The inverse of the square of 29,800 divided by 39,800 is 1.78, and the sales results were in keeping with this value.

Tokunaga remarks: "For us that price reduction was more of a means of carrying through with our purpose than a way of earning profits. That's what the game business is all about. That's why we thought things had to be done right. We received instructions from Sony, but in the end our enthusiasm exceeded Sony's."

Maruyama comments: "Even though a particular instruction may be a major issue for Sony for a time, for us the business is an ongoing, life-or-death concern. We think about the issues day and night, and we deliberately sustain the tension level. That is the decisive factor behind our resolve."

7

C H A P T E R

The Fight for Control in the United States

U.S. development of the American market is surely the high-light of the love-hate relationship between SCEI and Sony. It was a desperate struggle for supremacy. From the beginning, the two sides did not quite mesh. In such situations, the problem is manageable while the issues remain minor, but before long the gulf widens and eventually obstructs progress. American management came to raise objections and reject everything that was decided in Japan and eventually insisted that they would handle all matters concerning the market in the United States. As Kutaragi put it, "Our intentions and their judgments were at cross purposes every time."

The reason things had come to such a juncture is that authority over the U.S. market did not reside in Japan at the time. From the beginning, the Sony of America subsidiary included SEPC (Sony Electronic Publishing Company, New York), which, albeit in small quantities, produced Super Famicon and Sega Genesis games. This subsidiary was also given responsibility for licensing activities and marketing, as well as sales, for the PlayStation in the U.S. market. The problem was that the president of SEPC raised objections time and again to the actions taken in Japan.

First he objected to the color of the console. According to the designer Gotoh: "We took great pains in deciding the color. White is the color of computers, but that pertains to office computers. The PlayStation was an amusement computer, so we thought of giving it a different color. Black is the most common color for AV equipment, but black is too oppressive. That's why we decided on gray with a slight tinge of purple." Despite the care given to color selection, the Americans objected to it, refusing to accept a gray console. They insisted that gray was unacceptable in the U.S. market, and that the console must be white.

Neither did they like the design or the logo mark. Their approach was to object to everything on grounds such as the results of market research: "We can't accept such an unusual controller. The design is too small for American hands." Although Gotoh designed the controller to be appropriate for the global market, the very idea met with outright rejection from the Americans.

What is more, they insisted that they would set the U.S. list price themselves and they disapproved of the name PlayStation. The "Play" in PlayStation, they said, was reminiscent of "Playboy" and might be misconstrued. With one issue after another, the criticism was relentless. However, the most fundamental principle behind the PlayStation strategy was to promote one design and one product concept as a global standard, and for the United States to pursue an independent program was simply out of the question.

Regardless of how many problems arose, there could be no resolution, because SCEI in Japan and the Sony of America subsidiary SEPC were under different chains of management authority. As Kutaragi relates, "Moreover, the adversary was the president of Sony of America. I was just another employee." Kutaragi and the president of SEPC held completely different perceptions of the game business. Kutaragi had the confidence to implement an original business model at SCEI. But he and his colleagues had been prejudged. People in the United States were making comments like "You people don't have the ability. There's no place for Sony in the game market. It's Sega that will survive in the U.S.." The president of SEPC continually counseled even Ohga that Sony should cooperate with Sega. In fact, newspapers in the U.S. on May 20, 1993, gave extensive coverage to an SEPC announcement that it would offer software for the Sega platform.

The view of the president of SEPC was that Japan could be left alone as a unique market, but that the rest of the world was different. The U.S. market would be handled his way.

Because the PlayStation was a software business, responsibility for it should be unified under his management. The program would certainly fail if decisions were made out of his jurisdiction. His attitude was that, after all, Kutaragi and his crew were simply involved in the development and manufacture of the hardware, and they should manufacture as instructed and leave the marketing and other business issues to him.

The two sides were in particular disagreement concerning policy on software pricing. The Japanese wanted to lower software prices. But the American side insisted that prices must be raised. Discord arose over the differing views. Why were opinions so divided? U.S. executive management were all veterans of the game industry, and they decided everything based on existing models and past knowledge and experience. But the PlayStation represented the repudiation and overthrow of the status quo in the game industry. The two schools of thought were fundamentally and irrevocably different.

The situation can therefore be framed in terms of a dispute between traditionalists and innovators. The Japanese initially set the price of software at $58 to aim for market penetration and, in Kutaragi's words, "take advantage to the fullest" of the CD-ROM medium. For their part, SEPC management were united in the view that software prices must be set at a high level. Although the U.S. side also desired low prices as a matter of course, the decision was made to set prices at between $59 and $69 (subsequently to be lowered to the current level of between $39 and $49). This was the same price point as mask ROM cartridges, precluding the price differentiation made possible by the CD-ROM medium. The U.S. side took the same approach toward hardware pricing, antipathy at the notion of losing money leading to a desire to build a profit margin into the price.

Tokunaka summarized the situation this way: "We're working to rewrite the rules of the game. They're completely unaware of that. The strategy is to upset the status quo. Is it any wonder that from the Americans' perspective SCEI are newcomers to the game business and that the U.S. is their home turf?" Even when we explained that with CD-ROM it is possible to produce only as much replacement stock as can be sold, the Americans persisted in saying "That won't work in the U.S."

Without question, the U.S. market is different from the Japanese market in some respects. Software manufacturers sell directly to retailers, so a game-machine platform developer cannot purchase software for resale as in Japan. But the only thing that made this peculiar distribution structure possible in Japan was that Nintendo had complicated distribution there. It was true that CD-ROM repeat production wouldn't become possible overnight in the United States. That things were structurally different could not be denied.

Even so, the rift between Japan and the United States could not be ignored. As Tokunaka recalls: "At that time, in the spring of 1995, we were working under a triple handicap. Worries about exchange rates, which had shifted toward a dramatically stronger yen, the problems with management in the U.S., and the sluggish sales in Japan kept me from sleeping at night."

REGAINING CONTROL OF THE PLAYSTATION FROM SONY OF AMERICA

Unless SCEI sorted out the problems in the United States, the PlayStation could not succeed. Kutaragi's view was that everyone's attitude toward the United States was indecisive. Tokunaka was complaining, "Whatever you say, the responsibility for the U.S. lies with Sony of America...." At the same time, Maruyama was grumbling: "I'm not interested in anyplace other than Japan. Besides, it's all too much trouble. Management is different in the U.S., so why don't you just let them get on with it?"

To those opinions Kutaragi retorted: "This is no time to be weak-kneed. This is a format business aimed at the entire world, and the U.S. is the most important region. We have to somehow solve this problem to penetrate the U.S. market." He was insistent on this point at the informal directors' meetings held over lunch on Mondays. According to Maruyama, the sessions were "disorderly, exhausting free-for-alls. People rudely interfered with the affairs of others. Management meetings in ordinary Japanese companies are completely different. That's why everyone would be utterly exhausted after the discussions."

Kutaragi appealed to Ohga himself time and again that unless responsibility for the U.S. market were consolidated in Japan, the business couldn't possibly be successful. He also pleaded his case before an unreceptive management at Sony Music.

In the early days, there had been no infrastructure—and hence no choice but to start the business using Sony resources. However, things had reached the stage where the friction with local U.S. management could not be ignored. Lacking its own resources in the U.S., SCEI had no choice but to rely on Sony's resources to get started in the American market. However, the friction between SCEI and management of the Sony subsidiary in the U.S. had reached the point where it was threatening to hinder development of SCEI's business. SCEI had to take action. As quickly as possible, SCEI must bring responsibility for the U.S. market under the SCEI management umbrella so it could create a structure in which it could decide on the marketing and licensing of its own products. To forge ahead in the U.S. market, they must completely wrest control of the PlayStation away from Sony of America.

Maruyama was the first to understand: "It's time to regain control of the PlayStation from Sony of America!" he declared. He went on to say he would go to the United States to regain control himself. His view was that the capital relationship must be corrected and the business properly run.

The situation throughout Sony management had changed. Nobuyuki Idei had assumed the presidency of Sony and the president of Sony of America had resigned. It was May 22, 1995. The reorganization of Sony of America had begun. Now was the time!

FOUR DAYS PER WEEK IN THE UNITED STATES

"We must regain control of the U.S.," Kutaragi said, insisting that he himself go to the United States. But those around him put a stop to the idea, saying, "No. You have things to do in Japan."

Ultimately, Maruyama was chosen to go. It was 1996, and Sony Music's business performance had been less than ideal. Maruyama had been told, "We want you to concentrate on Sony Music's business," but he was also worried about the situation with the PlayStation in the United States.

Overseas business had always been outside the sphere of Sony Music's operations. Sony Music in New York was responsible for global operations outside of Japan, with the responsibility of the Japanese parent company limited to the domestic market. For this reason, Sony Music in Japan completely lacked expertise in overseas affairs. Responsibility for various aspects of the PlayStation business, including marketing, had shifted from Sony Music to SCEI, and overseas matters were no exception. Nevertheless, this was not a time for such concerns. The U.S. operation had to be rebuilt at all costs.

Although Maruyama was tapped to go, he retained his responsibilities at Sony Music in Tokyo and juggled the two jobs. He experimented with departing from Narita Airport on Wednesday and returning on Saturday, resting only on Sunday, but after three weeks of this he realized that he couldn't bear the physical strain. He switched to a schedule of Thursday departure from Narita, arrival in San Francisco at noon local time the same day, departing on Saturday, and arriving back at Narita on Sunday evening. He participated in management meetings on Monday at Sony Music and Tuesday at SCEI, and he worked at both jobs on Wednesday and Thursday. It was a horrendous routine. "It occupied all my attention, so it was no big deal. The funny thing is, there was no jet lag. I thought it was quite a feat myself. No doubt I was overly exhausted, though. After I stopped going, I slept ten hours a day for the next six months."

Maruyama's strength was his nimble footwork. He marched directly into the San Francisco office and began an investigation of the management staff's conduct of business. Although the Sony America president had resigned, the people actually involved with the PlayStation business had remained. Would they conduct themselves in accordance with the requirements of the Japanese operation?

Maruyama carefully assessed the likelihood that U.S. management would respect the intentions of management in Japan. He concluded that it would be impossible for managers steeped in the conventions of the game industry, and he decided to replace the lot except for a select few. In January of 1997, Sony established subsidiary SCEI America in San Francisco, simultaneously replacing most of the managers and launching a new management team. Maruyama comments: "We swept the organization clean of all of the old obstacles. We realized that we had to manage our own business."

This was no time to relax. Lack of focus at this time could well result in the loss of everything they had fought for and won. It was time for Kutaragi to step forward. He became chairman of SCEI America, and although he didn't hold to the grueling schedule Maruyama had maintained, he spent one week per month in San Francisco until the end of 1997.

"Success overseas became possible only because these changes were made," declares Kutaragi. The key factor was establishing a better approach to the software business. The first thing Kutaragi did was to discontinue preferential treatment of resellers that gave away software free of charge to customers who purchased the hardware. "This is something that must not be done in the software business. I vigorously persuaded the U.S. staff that software is not an accessory to the hardware."

The profit margin on hardware sales is slim, and a manufacturer cannot rely on recouping losses from sales of hardware with profits from software. That's why high-volume sales are so important. Products that don't sell are returned, but it's impossible to determine whether a product has been sold until it is confirmed that it hasn't been returned after three months. According to Kutaragi, "That's why we paid so much attention to stock levels."

The key is to develop a business model that delivers profits from hardware sales. Previously, Sony of America's marketing had been focused on selling the PlayStation through resellers with which it had a business relationship for Sony audiovisual products. In this distribution channel the overall margin and rebate structure is complicated, and the traditional business style is for these stores to sell from stock.

However, Kutaragi believed that distribution should be different for games and AV products. He knew that the time for targeting core game users was now past and that the next stage of mass popularization was approaching. Games are a format business that is grounded in widespread market penetration. It is suited to retailers that mass-advertise—say, by distributing large quantities of leaflets—and sell in high volume on a nationwide scale.

SCEI now shifted its sales foundation to mass merchandisers such as Wal-mart, K-mart, Toys-R-Us, and Sears.

Kutaragi visited Wal-mart headquarters in the Arkansas countryside on several occasions. He recalls that the PlayStation was popular within Wal-mart, but the firm was saying that persistent stock shortages were preventing it from putting much effort behind the product. "After several visits, they began to trust us at last. I told them repeatedly, 'I am ultimately responsible for the PlayStation in the U.S. I will assume responsibility for overseeing manufacture and support you. I would very much like for you to take on the product .'"

The tact required for this type of negotiation is no different from that in Japan. Kutaragi's approach was to persuade store management by saying: "We will undertake to ensure replenishment of stock. In return, we ask you to prepare a location in the store where the PlayStation will get the most exposure. We will also do this or that for you, so we want you to increase space in the showcase for the PlayStation." At times the mass merchandisers tried to defend themselves, but Kutaragi would continue to point out problems at these stores and to pursue concrete solutions. Kutaragi would often find time to visit resellers and investigate problems for himself. In most cases, the buyers eventually gave in and promised to make improvements in their approach to PlayStation sales.

Nevertheless, the purchase-for-resale system so characteristic of the PlayStation marketing strategy in Japan had been adopted for practically no software titles in the United States. This means that the developer of the platform had nearly no idea of the activities of software manufacturers, which distributed their own products. Says Masaru Kato (today executive director, Director Administration Division, SCEI), "It's a shame that the system that succeeded in Japan couldn't be transplanted as is to the U.S.." Kato attempted to persuade software manufacturers to change their marketing approach by saying, "It's senseless to manufacture high volumes based on forecasts and hold high levels of stock. A purchasing and sales system that permits consolidated distribution management is best suited to take advantage of the distinctive characteristics of the CD-ROM." But his efforts were to no avail.

Because manufacturing lead times for ROM cartridges are long, purchase orders must be made according to forecasts and stock must be held to meet long-term demand. Moreover, manufacturer overruns must be cleared out in the used-software market. Kato continues: "But verbal explanations to the effect that with CD-ROM you can assess the level of market demand and quickly manufacture only as much as the market requires fell on deaf ears. It's no different from missionary work. You travel around persuading people by providing a concrete example: 'Replenishment stock for this particular software title should be manufactured according to this schedule.' This type of persuasion, repeated over and over, breaks down preconceptions and gradually wins people over."

Although a platform developer is unable to purchase and resell software in the United States, it is permitted to invest in the titles of a software publisher. This gives the platform developer a voice in the software market. Furthermore, willingness on the part of the platform developer to invest in software titles would serve to make other software publishers aware of the advantages of the CD-ROM medium in manufacturing replenishment stock.

SCEI continued to tackle the problems from all angles, and its self-reliant effort to develop the market began to pay off during the second half of 1997. Because the market had been large from the start, once growth had begun, the breakthrough occurred rapidly.

The surge in sales finally came in the 1997 Christmas season, one year later than in Japan. The number of consoles sold in North America for the year ending in March 1997 was 3 million. In the year ending in March 1998, 7.7 million units were sold.

PURSUING A RAPID START IN EUROPE

Whereas regaining control was Sony's most important task for the U.S. market, the task in Europe was to painstakingly build a sales network from the ground up. As Kato explains: "In Europe, once an infrastructure is put in place, there are rich fields to cultivate. With Sega Saturn the ratio of sales between the United States and Europe is two to one. With the PlayStation it is five to four. This is due to the contribution of the Middle East and Eastern Europe. Infrastructure development was effective to that degree. Once a system has been established, implementation proceeds at high speed. This becomes a barrier to entry for manufacturers late to the market."

The key to the European strategy was to get the business up and running as quickly as possible. Preparations got under way at the end of 1994, only ten months ahead of the projected launch in the autumn of 1995. At that time no business systems were in place: no office, no sales force, no distribution. It was truly a case of starting from scratch.

Kato began by recruiting a management team. He appointed Chris Deerling, president of overseas operations at the sales subsidiary of Sony Picture Entertainment, to head up the European operation. Europe was structured much like the United States, with SCEI Europe established as a division within Sony Electronics Publishing. However, there was a major difference from the situation in the United States. In the words of Kato: "An extraordinarily smooth mutual understanding was established with Deerling. He is in large measure responsible for the success of the PlayStation in Europe."

Next SECI tackled the problem of distribution. Kato continues: "Time was short, so we used whatever came to hand, selecting among available Sony resources." They used warehouses that Sony Music maintained in the region. They couldn't service the equipment themselves, so they contracted service to the existing Sony service network. However, their reliance on Sony was limited to resource utilization. Still, this deliberate interaction with the parent company marked another fundamental difference from the situation in the United States.

Although the local Sony sales companies indicated interest in offering the product, they were turned down. Says Kato: "The structure of the game business is different from that of Sony's core AV business. Pricing, margin structure, rebate structure, everything ... the two businesses are very dissimilar. We place primary importance on the contribution from software sales. It's all right if we break even on hardware sales. In fact, we wouldn't mind much if we lost money on the hardware."

However, Europe is geographically widespread, and SCEI couldn't cover the entire territory with its own sales network. The Sony sales companies assumed responsibility for territories such as Eastern Europe, the Middle East, Russia, and Dubai. That they were Sony Group companies had no direct bearing on the decision; it was a matter of convenience and a way of buying time.   In April 1997, the management structure in each country was reshuffled. SCEI established sales subsidiaries in the United Kingdom, Germany, Italy, Spain, Switzerland, and Austria. At long last, they started to cultivate the market. Kato recalls: "The guys who joined Sony at the time always say my hair is grayer now. But I hardly remember facing hardships. I look back and think that we accomplished what we set out to do."

The wisdom of that strategy is evident in the financial results for the fiscal year ended March 1998: 9.64 million units sold, which far outstripped the 3 million units sold the preceding year. It goes without saying that this stellar performance in Europe represented a major contribution to Sony.

MAJOR BREAKTHROUGHS OVERSEAS
ALLEVIATE A CRISIS AT HOME

Establishment of overseas markets mitigated the effects of a crisis back in Japan. In the summer of 1997, the warehouses in Japan were groaning under the weight of between 500,000 and 600,000 PlayStation consoles. The reason for the excess stock was careless overproduction. First of all, sales forecasts had been overly optimistic. In January 1997, Square published the hit game Final Fantasy, which sold 3.5 million units and caused a two-month surge in PlayStation sales. The yearly PlayStation sales forecast, prepared at that time, called for sales of 7 million consoles in the coming year.

To be sure, monthly sales of PlayStation at the time were between 500,000 and 600,000 consoles, and monthly sales during the summer were projected to reach the 600,000 to 700,000 unit level. The annual sales forecast was fixed at 7 million units by multiplying 600,000 units by twelve months. This was an extraordinarily aggressive projection: Only 6.5 million units had been produced and shipped from the time of launch until March of 1996.

In complete defiance of the forecast, sales continued to slip with each passing month, then ground to a virtual halt in early summer. By the time it was recognized that something unusual was taking place, the inventory for September sales had already been manufactured. The realization that the Final Fantasy–fueled sales surge was a temporary phenomenon had come too late.

Production of the domestic model was completely discontinued from June to August, but unsold stock remained in the warehouses. The annual sales projection was reduced from 7 million to 5 million units. In the end, annual sales for fiscal 1997 were 4.99 million units.

So, what happened to the excess inventory? Some see it as divine intervention.

Sales rapidly took off in overseas markets due to Kutaragi and his team who had the foresight to develop overseas markets just in time to conteract the decrease in Japan, most notably sales through the major U.S. mass merchandisers Kutaragi had so persistently visited. Distributors began screaming about product shortages, and SCEI quickly shifted production earmarked for the domestic market to meet demand overseas. The excess inventory disappeared in an instant.

The timing of the surge in overseas sales was certainly fortuitous. As Shimamoto puts it: "This is without doubt what the game business is all about. Just when you think things couldn't possibly be worse, something miraculous happens. That's always been the way at Sony Music. When you're struggling to keep above water, the solution presents itself." Although it may seem that SCEI inherited this business intuition from Sony Music, the truth is that it was Kutaragi's strategy to fix production capacity and shift the emphasis of the business to overseas markets, taking advantage of the opportunity to forge ahead abroad when momentum in the Japanese market slowed.

Kutagari had visited the major mass merchandisers to personally promise that SCEI would provide a plentiful supply of the PlayStation. Thus reassured, the mass merchandisers began pouring their efforts into positioning the PlayStation for greater market visibility. The result was explosive sales that surpassed even Kutaragi's optimistic forecasts.

In Europe, the development of infrastructure now began to pay dividends as well. As in the United States, the game business improved and demands from resellers to ramp up production increased daily. In response, factories geared up to manufacture at full capacity. One after another, stores sold out of the PlayStation before year end. To meet the demand, SCEI chartered jumbo jets and planned for production right up to the end of the year.

It was a breakthrough for the PlayStation game machine of global significance.

8

Kutaragi's Venture Business Advice for the Entrepreneur

After his chance encounter with System G, Ken Kutaragi conceived the PlayStation and proceeded to elevate his creation by working like a man possessed. First came the failed joint development proposal with Nintendo, then Sony's decision to proceed with the project independently, algorithm development, hardware development, finalization of the business plan, recruitment of software developers, and the struggle for control with management in the United States.

Responding to Kutaragi's single-minded desire, Sato devised the "purchase-for-resale" distribution model, which revolutionized the game industry, Gotoh achieved his timeless hardware designs, Maruyama injected considerable business expertise cultivated at Sony Music, and Tokunaka diligently steered the business with a firm and steady hand.

Kutaragi is the father of the PlayStation, and the PlayStation is Kutaragi's child. What decisions did Kutaragi make during the various stages of the project, and what was on his mind as he put them into practice? Let us consider the nine business principles of Kutaragi, the man of whom Ohga said: "Without Kutaragi's unyielding spirit, PlayStation wouldn't be what it is today." A look at these nine conditions for success also provides insight into the reasons behind the success of the PlayStation project.

CONDITION 1: PERFECTION IS ATTAINABLE, ESPECIALLY FOR THE SALARIED EMPLOYEE

Says Kutaragi: "After all, one person alone can't do much. You need to work with others to accomplish something big." Kutaragi's original concept was not to operate as an independent venture business, but to set up a venture business within a corporation. His reasoning was that there is a limit to what a small-scale company can do to achieve rapid growth. A venture business that reaches $100 million in annual sales is said to be highly successful, but Kutaragi thought on a far larger scale.

Kutaragi was born the son of a tradesman. He experienced the fascination of involvement in an independent business when he helped with his father's business as a child. That's a big reason why he became interested in establishing an even bigger business and took up this challenge at Sony. Kutaragi was preoccupied with being "a member of a corporation and an entrepreneur." In his words: "This type of perfection is attainable even within an existing large corporation. I wanted to show everyone that salaried employees were best suited to achieve this type of success. I wanted to prove through a real-world case what even a mere company employee could achieve with a dream, desire, strategy, and superb colleagues."

Kutaragi is by no means an exemplary corporate employee. There are many people even within Sony who can't accept his way of doing things. When he first joined Sony, he was just another engineer. But as he says: "I thought it would be great if everyone could take courage from the thought that even that guy, even a salaried businessman, can accomplish that much." The success of Kutaragi's project is proof that what can't be accomplished by a privately held venture business can be done within a major corporation.

CONDITION 2: USE ALL RESOURCES AVAILABLE TO YOU

Kutaragi pursued speed. "Not $100 million in ten years—$100 million in one year" was his goal. Another way of putting it: "The objective is to accomplish in five years what took Sony fifty years." There is, in fact, no other example of a venture business that in four years after launch had realized $700 million in consolidated global sales. This did not happen by chance; it was a thoroughly intended result. In Kutaragi's words: "Everyone comments on how suddenly the PlayStation business has grown, but from our perspective it had to be this way. The video game business is a platform business. That's why the developer must waste no time in establishing the platform's viability."

This extraordinary growth rate was achieved with the strategy of "using all resources available." It takes a great deal of time to establish a venture business from scratch. To attain rapid growth, venture business managers use all available resources. This refers to sources of personnel, outsourced manufacturing partners, and sources of capital.

Among the resources Kutaragi tapped into was Ohga's anger. Kutaragi ingeniously harnessed the energy generated by the anger Ohga felt at having had his face rubbed in the mud by Nintendo, and during the meeting at which the issue of whether Sony should independently enter the game market was finally discussed, he caused Ohga to pound the table and shout "DO IT!"

CONDITION 3: HOW TO GATHER PEOPLE FOR YOUR VENTURE

Venture businesses find it difficult to attract talented people. During the early stages, two or three founders work hard as the core of the business, but as they attempt to grow the business, they overextend themselves.

Says Kutaragi: "Working hard at a venture business can bring annual sales of $100 million. If you are resourceful, you might be able to achieve $500 million. But you won't get any further. That's because you can't inject a sufficient number of talented people into the business. But we were able to take our pick of staff from our former workplaces."

During the recruiting activities at SCEI, each man invited staff from his former workplace. Maruyama scouted software and marketing talent from Sony Music, Tokunaka brought in management, legal, and general administrative expertise, and Kutaragi raided research centers to assemble a staff of engineers.

Was it a simple matter to assemble a team of engineers from the research centers? Kutaragi's response to this question is: "Sure it was simple. It is the nature of engineers to be attracted to work that they really want to do, work that is more fantastic than what they are currently doing; they will always flock to a more stimulating objective."

Sony is a company that spent fifty years involved in the fields of analog audio and video. Each business division has a full allotment of mechanism and analog circuit engineers. However, divisions are profit centers, and stealing away engineers who produce profits is difficult. But the research centers are cost centers. If they shed staff, they reduce their costs. That's why it is relatively simple to obtain staff from research centers. That was Kutaragi's approach.

Maruyama, who was responsible for recruiting from Sony Music, does not remember a particular moment when he decided to bring aboard a lot of people. The Epic Sony game unit was a bit overstaffed, Maruyama had tacit approval to invite people to join SCEI, and so the number of staff at the PlayStation game unit grew. Maruyama explains: "Even if a company desires talented personnel, the best people are loath to make a change. That's why the trick in starting up a new business is to seek out people who can do the job but who have somehow fallen behind the times, or who don't get along with their managers, or who don't seem to have much to do."

Two exceptional people will not develop in the same section of a company at the same time. That's why a talented person who seems to have time on his hands is attractive to a new venture. He is capable of doing good work, but he is underutilized and has a store of energy. All you have to do is to touch a flame to that energy. Akira Sato is an example. The area for which he was responsible was eliminated, and he was killing time in the Yokohama Sales Office when Maruyama reeled him in.

Sony vice president Iba says: "When Kutaragi said he wanted this person or that one, I just shut up and gave them to him. I turned them over to him unconditionally." From the beginning, Sony had a good people to provide when SCEI requested staff. Because Iba had overall authority over planning, he could transfer staff involved in this area. Tokunaka is an example. In Iba's words: "If you're going to staff up a unit, you don't invest in dribs and drabs. My policy is to go all out if I think it's required."

CONDITION 4: WORK INDEPENDENTLY FROM THE MOTHERSHIP (SONY)

SCEI was both a venture within a corporation and an external venture. It is a venture within a corporation in that it was capitalized by Sony and Sony Music. But it can be called an external venture in that it was able to operate independently of the joint shareholders. In Kutaragi's view, "That we were not required to consult with the parent company over every little thing and were able to take decisions independently was a factor behind the success of the business."

Kutaragi decided to become a hanger-on at the Epic Sony New Media Department in Aoyama to avoid interference from the parent company. There was an MSX group as well as a group promoting Phillips CD/I, and neither group looked favorably on Kutaragi's project. Kutaragi recalls: "That's why from my point of view it was extremely valuable to escape the interference within Sony and come to Aoyama."

It was also fortunate for Kutaragi that the area in which he involved himself was the game business, which was a forte of neither Sony nor Sony Music. That the new media business unit which made games at Sony Music did not develop into a business division was another stroke of luck; becoming a business division would have brought profit responsibility and the unit would not have been able to freely pursue its activities.

CONDITION 5: FORM A GROUP OF LIKE-MINDED COMRADES AND PARTITION YOURSELVES OFF

Kutaragi says, "A condition of success was that we did everything ourselves, no matter the circumstances." When a company has capital, it can buy technology or buy ideas, but under those circumstances its activities can't be considered true ventures. First, the principals must develop their own business model and then move forward with it, trusting their own judgment and leaving no decisions. Kutaragi continues: "You will succeed because you have formed a group of superb colleagues. Doing what you want to do brings a feeling of satisfaction. Working in a pleasant environment gives rise to lots of ideas." He refers to the passage through the stages of headlong involvement in the Nintendo project, the collapse of the project, and the subsequent decision to embark independently on a perilous business venture.

How dangerous would it have been to rely on the judgment of others? One way of answering this is to look at the seemingly endless discord SCEI experienced with local management over marketing in the United States. "Businesses are made by people. When you're able to work with superb colleagues, you can produce superb results. Look at the *Titanic*. Even such an enormous ocean liner will sink if you put a little iceberg in its path. It's because the ship is so big that it can't be steered at will."

If strategy has been determined through agreement among colleagues, you stay the course no matter what happens, even if things don't proceed as planned for a time. For example, after the breakdown in the talks with Nintendo, Sony didn't for a moment consider entering into an alliance with Sega.

CONDITION 6: TRENDS WILL ALWAYS HAVE UPS AND DOWNS

Kutaragi foresaw the future, plotted a course, drew up a business scenario, advocated his views, and assembled like-minded people. How could he foresee the future? He explains it this way: "I'm confident in matters of technology. That's my hobby, and I consider myself second to none in these matters."

Kutaragi's true vocation was that of a businessman—he had worked in one business or another from an early age—but his pastime was technology. His specialty was semiconductors and computers. He says: "It's preferable not to have an area of specialty. When you have a specialty, your field of vision narrows. This is dangerous."

Kutaragi doesn't believe anything he doesn't understand. That's why he is always studying. He even reads academic theses. He explains: "I don't like it when there is a gap in my knowledge. At present I'm interested in the Emotion Synthesizer (this appears to be a computer technology for expressing emotions, but Kutaragi says he is unable to reveal the details at this time). The first thing I do in studying a new technological sector is to take an overview. Then I go into detail. This order is important. If you delve into each and every detail from the beginning, you can't see the overall situation. I don't make notes. I can remember important points which need to be remembered without notes. I just let myself forget everything else. Making notes just causes stress. What's committed to memory is useful for making judgments."

Kutaragi's view of contemporary times is simple: Trends will always have ups and downs. "Things are bound to change," he says. "This creates mountains and valleys. For example, Sony mythology is repeatedly destroyed and recreated in six-year cycles. It's the same with semiconductors and with market securities: Everything is cyclical."

In 1994, when computer memory prices had stabilized at a high level, Tokunaka and Maruyama were extremely worried. But Kutaragi was unperturbed. He watched the trends in the personal computer industry and determined that memory prices would fall eventually. He says: "It is an obvious principle that if the mountain is high, the valley is sure to be low. I said at the time personal computers were in fashion that sales were bound to slump in the future. That became a reality."

"Losses are investments. In the capitalist world losses are inevitable in the early stages of an investment, and what's important is to ascertain where those losses are to be recouped. Even if you fail, in the end that becomes an investment: You make sure that when you look back on the situation, you can think that the failure paved the way for your current success. If the valley is low, the mountain will be high."

CONDITION 7: STRIVING FOR QUALITY WILL SUPPORT YOUR FORESIGHT CAPABILITIES

Around 1987 Kutaragi was interested in synthesizer sound. That was the time the Yamaha DX7 and Casio Tone appeared on the market. The disk system Nintendo was using at the time was based on FM sound generation, but the sound produced by the Sony PCM generator was several times better.

Kutaragi decided to try to sell the PCM sound generator to Nintendo, but it would come down to a contest between FM and PCM. Just how good was the sound of PCM? The signal-to-noise ratio of FM sound generators is only about forty to fifty decibels, which means a high level of noise. Compared to this, PCM delivers eighty-two decibels. "Without exception, everyone who listened to the sound was astonished," says Kutaragi.

"It didn't seem like video game audio. I still have a DAT recording of the first sound generated in May of 1989 as a keepsake."

Kutaragi was moving the audio technology from FM to PCM. Today PCM sound generation is a commonplace technology, but in those days it was revolutionary. While Kutaragi's preference for PCM may have arisen from his personal desire to hear good-quality sound, it was also an indication that Kutaragi had foreseen the potential of the technology.

There is another story. In 1985, one corporate project at Sony was development of CCD (charge-coupled device). CCDs were first used in 8mm video cameras and their use later became widespread. Kutaragi, at that time involved with development of the Mavicam digital camera, made a request of the CCD development team: "Will you make a progressive CCD for me?" The response was a look of incredulity. CCD development was in its early stages, and it was all the development team could do to produce CCDs for interlaced scanning (which scan every other line) used in animation. They hadn't even begun to work with progressive scanning CCDs with twice the vertical resolution. Currently Sony is the largest player in progressive CCD technology with its CCDs for digital still cameras, but at the time no one had even conceived of progressive CCDs. Kutaragi explains: "Why, of course everyone wants to view high-quality images. It is only natural for a technician to propose positive developments."

The breakthrough in the use of progressive-scanning CCDs was to come about ten years later, with their use in digital still cameras. That the world moves in the direction of an increased emphasis on quality is the bedrock of foresight.

CONDITION 8: USE FORESIGHT LITTLE BY LITTLE

Kutaragi exercises foresight, but by no means does he reveal everything he foresees to others. Many corporate executives are highly suspicious, don't listen to others, and believe nothing that falls outside their own successful experiences. How does one go about convincing this type of high-level manager? In Kutaragi's view: "Under no circumstances do you mention the whole scenario. If there are a hundred, you mention only two or three at first. If you envision the next ten steps, you take one step and create a situation where the second step can be seen. In so doing, you give evidence that you can see two steps ahead and instill confidence in management. But if you explain all ten steps from the beginning, they will wonder what in the world you are thinking and won't believe the first thing you say."

In other words, you reveal foresight little by little in accordance with the other party's ability to understand it. The more revolutionary the topic, the greater is the potential for being misunderstood if you reveal too much in the beginning.

This approach is useful not only in persuading a manager but also when working as part of a team. Kutaragi puts it this way: "There are times when, although you think a person will help to advance your cause, you are concerned they will misunderstand if you explain everything at once. That's when you limit what you say and make an effort to adjust your words to suit the listener. You create leeway by advising what you would do in a given situation, and when the work is subsequently completed, the team grows in confidence. There's only so much each individual can do, but confident people can accomplish great things."

Even the decision to launch PlayStation on December 3, 1994, was in accordance with Kutaragi's calculations. Long before then, he had been convinced that this was the only possible time to launch the game machine. And he was pleased to go along when everyone else at SECI came to the same conclusion, though he told no one of his own thinking on the subject. "You arrange things so that everyone thinks that way. When things go well, you comment on your good fortune. It's a great feeling when something is accomplished and everyone thinks that the success is the result of their own ideas."

That's the key to success when working as part of a team. You arrange things so that everyone feels that what was accomplished was due to their own participation. When you do that, incredible power is accumulated. As in the fable about the north wind and the sunshine, you accomplish nothing by becoming the cold north wind and forcing people to work. Rather, you're better off by becoming the sun and providing a warm breeze and sunshine. Because you are planning ahead based on foresight, you can act the role of the sun.

Maruyama says: "Previously you could understand the trends in the game market by looking at the Famicon or Super Famicon model. However, there was no precedent as to how to develop the PlayStation business. Everything was in Kutaragi's head. That's why not even we understand. That's why in the end everyone gets caught in Kutaragi's trap and has to fall in line with his intentions."

When the furor over the PlayStation price reduction occurred, Maruyama and others at SCEI said to the people in the Sony parent company, "What's wrong with reducing the price?" This only served to heighten the controversy. Says Maruyama: "Kutaragi never missed an opportunity to tell us that computer prices were bound to fall because the price of memory would drop. That's why we thought that at some time it would be only natural to reduce the price of the PlayStation." It was the spring of 1995, and prospects for sales of the PlayStation had become grim. The decision reached at an informal directors meeting was that something had to be done: The price would be reduced by $100. "It was decided all at once," Maruyama continues. "It wasn't just me. Kutaragi's lessons on the nature of the computer business had been driven home with everyone."

Maruyama and the others thought that Kutaragi had explained to the people at Sony that computer prices were bound to fall. That's why they responded, "Price reductions are totally natural with game machines" when Sony people who feared a price reduction posed hard questions. This only served to add fuel to the fire, because Kutaragi had said nothing to the people at Sony.

CONDITION 9: PLAN THE EVOLUTION PROCESS

Kutaragi's way of dealing with people did not involve pressuring them into working; rather, he believed in creating an environment in which people would work voluntarily and in good spirits. This approach also is evident in Kutaragi's determination to create for game creators an environment that would allow them to be productive. The tool by which this was accomplished was the development software library, a concept that had come to Kutaragi soon after he joined Sony while he was working in audio development. Kutaragi had focused his attention not just on hardware but also on software development, and had devoted his efforts to preparing tools that reflected the opinions of front-line users. In this way he had contributed greatly to the competitive position of Sony's audio products.

With the development of the PlayStation, as well, Kutaragi vowed to develop tools that would make the environment for software creators pleasant. So he assembled a large group of digital engineers from within Sony and put them to work on this task. This resulted in the software library, which in turn facilitated software development for the PlayStation platform. Kutaragi and his team developed the library in parallel with the hardware—if anything, they put more effort into the library—and established a policy of top-to-bottom support of developers. This policy was implemented first and foremost as a means of ensuring a constant supply of new software for the platform.

"Content necessarily evolves, but for creators both time and good spirits are finite," Kutaragi says. "When it comes down to it, thinking up fresh ideas is troublesome, and in the end the number of products in the same genre tends to increase. Avoiding that situation hinges on coming up with ways to assist game creators in coming up with the new game ideas. The decision to prepare the development tools and the library arose out of the concept of finding ways to avoid limiting the number of new ideas and ways to develop those ideas."

The tools and library were prepared because they were required to get the PlayStation project up and running, but there was, in fact, a far more forward-thinking strategy at work as well. Because software content necessarily becomes more sophisticated and complicated over time, eventually a technical gap appears between the hardware format and the technical level demanded by the software content. It is an important function of the library to bridge that gap. In other words, the library is necessary for developing more advanced software under the existing format.

And there was an even more strategic objective. The various software programs that SCEI accumulated when it developed the library became a valuable archive for use in creating the next generation of hardware. Over time, a great many programs accumulated in the library as a result of the process of responding to user questions and the resulting demand for new software that arose.

That expertise and essential knowledge is itself video game IP (intellectual property), and IP can be incorporated into next-generation hardware. Using the analogy of a personal computer, this process is the same as upgrading the computer platform's operating system by incorporating the information and expertise gathered while using the existing operating system.

The library doesn't exist merely to support game creators. It is a means of creating on a day-to-day basis the IP to support future developments

EPILOGUE

When Ken Kutaragi embarked on the PlayStation project, everyone expected that it would fail. He was told that to do battle with the enormous Nintendo empire would be ill-advised. He was told to abandon the idea for his own good. Despite these cautions, Kutaragi accepted the challenge of making PlayStation the game-machine industry's top platform. And with the help of numerous clever business strategies to further his goals, he succeeded. Today Sony's PlayStation has conquered the world of video games.

Sony's Norio Ohga, the man who successfully commercialized the CD and MD media, says that based on his personal experience, "to be profitable, a closed format is necessary. But to make a success of a proprietary format is extremely difficult." Kutaragi succeeded at this difficult challenge.

Tokunaka, who conducted numerous business simulations while planning the venture, says: "It was an enormous success not predicted in any of the simulations."

Maruyama describes Kutaragi's success this way: "We were fortunate that we were amateurs and faced no obstacles. Although it is a truly fearsome industry, we were amateurs when it comes to games and we naively went about doing what we thought would be sure to work. Of course, people ridiculed us because we were amateurs, but our proposals later garnered support. We were not preoccupied with established industry practices—we started from square one and let the ideas flow freely and without restriction."

Today, PlayStation users can be found in many segments of the population. Ohga seems pleased when he says, "There has even been an increase among middle-aged users. The PlayStation has become popular among department managers at major corporations. No sooner do they get home from work than they shut themselves up in their rooms in front of the PlayStation. They play *Final Fantasy*. When their wives call out, 'It's time for dinner,' they spend a few minutes with the family over dinner, but they are soon back in their rooms again. I never imagined during the early stages that something like that might happen."

Even Ohga plays with the PlayStation. He likes the title *Go By Train!*, published by Taito. Says Sato, "This was the first software personally requested by Chairman Ohga." With this software if you don't operate the train correctly, you can't stop at the correct place at the station platform, and if this goes on, you lose your operator qualifications. To avoid that, you practice operating the train at rural stations on a railway in the mountains before taking charge of a train on Tokyo's busy Yamanote loop line. Ohga, who drives sports cars and can pilot a jet, derives great enjoyment from this heartwarming game software. He comments: "It's really difficult. But the fact is I never imagined that such an interesting game would become available."

Ohga, perhaps inspired by his experience with Go By Train!, says of the next-generation PlayStation: "If the previous game machines were narrow-gauge railroads, the PlayStation is a wide-gauge game format. Because the tracks are wide, there are numerous unknown possibilities. The proof of that is the various titles being published that no one could even imagine before. The next-generation PlayStation will soar through the air. It may even soar into space."

So, what does Kutaragi have up his sleeve for the Play-Station platform? In his own words: "The computer embodies the most advanced technology developed by the human race. It is on the same level as, or superior to, such inventions as

Watt's steam engine and Gutenberg's printing press. And it has only been a quarter of a century since we obtained them. Future developments will far outstrip anything we can predict. I want to further accelerate the speed of this information revolution. The PlayStation represents a single, entry-level method of achieving that goal; its place is as a technology driver toward that end. Games are nothing more than the first step, and the goal for the PlayStation is to provide an entire world of computerized home entertainment." In other words, when the PlayStation reaches its final form, people will be able to understand that it was a step toward that goal.

Says Kutaragi: "The current PlayStation represents achievement of about 30 percent of the ultimate objective. There are many days ahead. There are about one hundred different checkpoints. I'll just head straight down the road toward that goal."

Upon hearing these words, Maruyama's response was "What? One hundred checkpoints? Only 30 percent? It's the first I've heard that kind of talk!"

That's Ken Kutaragi's way of winning people's hearts.

G L O S S A R Y

3-DO A multimedia platform developed by The 3DO Company of the United States. CD-ROM was used as the storage medium. Matsushita Electric unsuccessfully promoted the platform.

Arcade game As opposed to home-use games, denotes game machines and game-machine software used in game arcades.

Architecture The basic software structure of a computer system.

C programming language A programming language developed for writing UNIX-based operating systems. It uses simple expressions and is easy to write.

Digital Dream Kids A Sony internal slogan proposed by President Nobuyuki Idei upon his appointment, it is a rallying cry to employees to create a company that "makes the digital dream come true."

Digital filter Method of filtering (blocking or allowing passage of signals of a certain frequency). Digital filtering permits far more accurate operation and control than the analog method.

Disk system A peripheral device for Nintendo's Famicon. A disk storage system that permits the user to save game data.

Dragon Quest An example of a Japanese RPG (role-playing game) produced by game manufacturer Enix.

DSP Digital signal processing unit. Uses software to carry out digital signal processing operations for various purposes.

Electroluminescence (EL) A procedure whereby a membrane of fluorescent material is formed on a glass plate and made luminescent by applying electric voltage via a transparent electrode. It is difficult to achieve full-color displays with EL.

FM sound generator A sound generator that reproduces sounds by means of frequency modulation. Yamaha drew attention to this method by adopting it for its DX7 Synthesizer.

Gate array A semifinished LSI circuit. Special capabilities can be built in to meet customer specifications.

IBM PC A 16-bit PC developed by IBM, which adopted Microsoft's operating system MS-DOS. It used an open platform that allowed any manufacturer to make compatible PCs, resulting in today's dominance of IBM compatibles in the PC market.

Image synthesizer A system used to produce computer graphics.

Large characters Large characters (people, etc.) that appear on the computer game screen.

LSI circuit Large Scale Integrated circuit. Applications include CPUs (central processing units) and memory.

Mavica A floppy disk digital camera. The consumer version of this camera went on sale in 1988. It attracted attention with the catchphrase "You don't need film anymore." "Mavica" is an abbreviation of "magnetic video camera."

Mega CD Sega's 16-bit game platform

MSX An 8-bit home computer jointly developed by Microsoft and ASCII. Sony and other consumer electronics companies participated in its commercialization, but it proved to be unsuccessful.

NEWS A Sony UNIX workstation that became a hit product in the mid-1980s. Regarded as an easy-to-use computer, it dominated the market for some years.

Nintendo 64 A 64-bit, home-use game platform developed jointly by Silicon Graphics of the United States and Nintendo.

Optical peak level meter A meter that displays peak level (highest volume of sound). Optical devices such as LCD and LED meters are the most common.

Overlay Overlapping layers of images on top of a base image. This makes image synthesis possible, and therefore achieves complex visual image expression.

PC Engine Developed by NEC, a home-use game machine utilizing CD-ROM technology. The first version was released in 1987, a CD-ROM–compatible extension in 1988.

PCM sound generator A "pulse-controlled modulation" sound generator that samples and reproduce sounds by means of digital signal processing.

Plasma display A direct-view display that utilizes vacuum discharge. Thin, large screens can be made by this method, and future growth in demand is anticipated for wall-mounted plasma TVs.

Quarter-L A brand name for Sony business-use personal computers.

Sega Saturn Sega's 32-bit game platform, which was released in November 1994. It caused a stir when it first came out, but it is now a minor player in the game-machine market.

SOBAX The world's first electronic calculator, released by Sony in 1967. Sony was later embroiled in a price war and eventually had to withdraw from the calculator market.

Sony of America The U.S. subsidiary of Sony. Sometimes abbreviated as Sony America.

Texture mapping Texture refers to substance. In computer graphics, texture mapping involves drawing lifelike images on the surface of objects (a person, monster, etc.) being created to give them a realistic look.

Volume unit (VU) meter A meter that measures changes in the level of sound input by a tape recorder. Most VU meters use needles for the level display.

INDEX